Portions of this program were used experimentally by the following teachers and their classes. The helpful criticism of these teachers and their students has affected the final form this book has taken.

Saundra N. Gross
Audubon Junior High School
Milwaukee, Wisconsin

Robert Harms
Wilson Junior High School
San Diego, California

Hilda V. Heim
Ellicott City Middle School
Ellicott City, Maryland

Carol Kocher
Tillicum Junior High School
Bellevue, Washington

LaJuana Nutt
Tift County Junior High School
Tifton, Georgia

Mike H. Ruggles
Miami Country Day and Resident School for Boys
Miami, Florida

This book was reviewed by the following teachers. Their criticisms also helped in the final preparation of materials. We gratefully acknowledge the critical assistance of:

Juanita Abernathy
English and Reading Coordinator
Department of Education, State of Georgia
Atlanta, Georgia

Evelyn Bullington
Miami Edison Middle School
Miami, Florida

James Sabol
Coordinator for English Language
Bellevue Public Schools
Bellevue, Washington

Mary Wilcoxon
Junior High School Resource Teacher
San Diego City Schools
San Diego, California

ALVIN A. LEE
Professor of English
McMaster University
Hamilton, Ontario, Canada

HOPE ARNOTT LEE
Formerly, teacher, grades 7-12
Dundas, Ontario, Canada

CIRCLE OF STORIES: ONE

Supervisory Editor
NORTHROP FRYE
University Professor
University of Toronto

General Editor
W. T. JEWKES
Professor of English
The Pennsylvania State University

HARCOURT BRACE JOVANOVICH, INC.
New York   Chicago   San Francisco   Atlanta   Dallas

ACKNOWLEDGMENTS: For permission to reprint copyrighted material, grateful acknowledgment is made to the following sources:

Margaret Atwood: "After the Flood, We" from *The Circle Game* by Margaret Atwood. Published by The House of Anansi.

Cambridge University Press, American Branch: Genesis 2: 5-25 and 3: 1-24 from *The New English Bible,* © The Delegates of The Oxford University Press and The Syndics of The Cambridge University Press, 1961, 1970. John 1: 1-5 from *The New English Bible, New Testament,* © The Delegates of The Oxford University Press and The Syndics of The Cambridge University Press, 1961, 1970.

Constable Publishers, London: "O strong of heart" (Boethius) from *Medieval Latin Lyrics,* translated by Helen Waddell.

The Dial Press: From "Down at the Cross" (retitled: "Life is tragic . . .") from *The Fire Next Time* by James Baldwin, copyright © 1962, 1963 by James Baldwin.

The Dolmen Press Limited: "The World" from *Medieval Irish Lyrics,* translated by James Carney.

E. P. Dutton & Co., Inc.: "Not Poor, Just Broke" from the book *Nigger: An Autobiography* by Dick Gregory with Robert Lipsyte, copyright, ©, 1964 by Dick Gregory Enterprises, Inc. Published by E. P. Dutton & Co., Inc.

E. P. Dutton & Co., Inc. and *The Bodley Head:* "The Coming of Connla" from the book *The Hound of Ulster* by Rosemary Sutcliff, copyright, ©, 1963 by Rosemary Sutcliff. Published by E. P. Dutton & Co., Inc. "How Finn Won His Father's Place" from the book *The High Deeds of Finn Mac Cool* by Rosemary Sutcliff, copyright, ©, 1967 by Rosemary Sutcliff. Published by E. P. Dutton & Co., Inc.

Faber and Faber Limited: Excerpt from "Listen. Put on morning" from *The White Threshold* by W. S. Graham.

v

Prentice-Hall, Inc.: "The Trees They Do Grow High" from the book *Songs of Man* by Norman Luboff and Win Stracke, © 1965 by Walton Music Corporation. Published by Prentice-Hall, Inc., Englewood Cliffs, New Jersey.

Random House, Inc.: "Riders to the Sea" from *The Complete Works of John M. Synge.* "A Soft November Night" from *Poems For Music,* by Robert Hillyer, copyright 1947 by Robert Hillyer.

The Literary Trustees of Walter de la Mare, and *The Society of Authors as their representative:* "All That's Past" and "The Listeners" from *The Complete Poems of Walter de la Mare 1970.*

The University of Nebraska Press: "The Coming of the Plague" from *The Collected Poems of Weldon Kees,* copyright 1960 John A. Kees.

Henry Z. Walck, Inc.: "The Story of Zal" from *Dragons, Unicorns and Other Magical Beasts* by Robin Palmer, copyright © 1966 by Robin Palmer.

Photographic Acknowledgments
p. 7, Ylla, Rapho-Guillumette; 16, Fay, FPG; 33, Gullers, Rapho-Guillumette; 41, Bettmann, Springer Film Archive; 46, Gossage, FPG; 51, Shelburne Museum, Shelburne, Vt.; 52, photo: John Freeman, London; 53, The Cleveland Museum of Art, Gift of Harold T. Clark in Memory of Mrs. William B. Sanders; 54, © United Feature Syndicate; 70, Davidson, Magnum; 85, The Museum of Modern Art — Film Stills Archive; 105, Riboud, Magnum; 118-119, The Museum of Modern Art, photo: Edward Steichen; 132-133, by Permission of the Trustees of Dickens House, London; 152, Ringdahl, DPI; 160, Morath, Magnum; 172-173, © Valley Daily News, Tarentum, Pa., by John Filo; 187, Scala, New York/Florence; 188, Georges Rouault, "Christ Mocked by Soldiers," 1932, oil on canvas, 36¼ x 28½", collection, The Museum of Modern Art, New York; 189, Winslow Homer, "The Gulf Stream," The Metropolitan Museum of Art, Wolfe Fund, 1906; 190, George Tooker, "The Subway" (detail), egg tempera on composition board, 1950, 18⅛ x 36⅛", collection, Whitney Museum of American Art, New York; 204, The British Museum, London; 220-221, James Karales © Look Magazine; 230, Paris Match, Pictorial Parade; 233, The Metropolitan Museum of Art, Harris Brisbane Dick Fund, 1943; 246, Library of Congress, photo: Dorothea Lange; 255, Christopher Johnson, Somerville, Mass.; 265, UPI.

Illustration Acknowledgments
pp. 2-3, Kenneth Longtemps; 138, letter cut on wood, from a "winged dragon series," printer of the Abusé en Court, Lyons, 1483; 139, miniature from the margin of a manuscript of an early fourteenth-century Latin Apocalypse; 140, top, lantern silhouette, China, bottom, bird god, Peruvian design; 141, shadow-play figures, Mameluke Egypt, fourteenth century; 142-143, Kenneth Longtemps; 270, goldwork, Panama; 271, wooden mask, Seneca Indian; 272, Elisabeth Kessler.

Authors' Preface

In addition to the teachers and students who have tested this material in their classrooms, *Circle of Stories* has, from its beginning, been blessed with generous help. We wish to express our gratitude to the following:

Jay Macpherson for suggestions, comments, and services too many and too varied to list.

Our editor, Kathleen Daniel, without whose midwifery this book would never have seen the light of day.

Ronald Campbell, for encouragement and guidance, and Joseph Loughman, Elisabeth Kessler, and Bernadette Pascucci for help in production.

Catherine Bankier, Madge Allwood, and Juliette Allan, librarians at the Dundas Public Library, for both their professional expertise and their enthusiasm.

Friends and colleagues whose libraries were raided and brains picked, among whom are: Amanda Bankier, Helen and Andrew Brink, Emily Cain, Mary Campbell, Janet Edmonstone, Audrey Gibson, Pat Kemp, Ethel Lymn, Jean McKay, Lamont Tilden, Nancy Vichert, Lisa Volkov, and Margaret and George Wallace.

Northrop Frye, our first and best university teacher.

Finally, our children, who constantly reminded us of the underlying purpose of our text, to educate the imagination, and whose shining imaginations taught us how to go about it.

Hope and Alvin Lee

Introduction

The imagination that has produced the poems and stories of the world operates on every age level: it has a childlike aspect, a youthful aspect, and so on up to an aspect of ancient wisdom.

In literature, we discover the world that our imaginations have already constructed. When poets and storytellers talk about the cycles of human life, about the beginning of things long ago, or about wish and nightmare, they are using the same set of building blocks that we use ourselves, from infancy to old age. What we discover in the poets we recognize as what we already know, but we can never know that we know it without them.

We live in society by means of our imaginations: it is the imagination that tells us how to react to the news, how to vote, how to choose a life-style. This imagination is part of a social vision: it tells us how we want to dress ourselves, for example, because our clothes dramatize our social attitudes.

Society is full of people who want to "capture" our imaginations, by propaganda, by advertising, by entertainment. When we read poets who want nothing from us except a response to something we already have, we see that the imagination is not to be learned from the outside; it is something to be released from the inside.

Our earliest poets in English used to speak of "unlocking the word hoard," and the reader of this book may now turn this page and that key at the same time.

N. F.

CONTENTS

FIRST STORY

Beginnings

Innocence

The Quest

The Power of Innocence

Withdrawal from Action

Survival, and the Telling of Tales

SECOND STORY

Destruction of the Beautiful

The Death of Innocence

Triumph and Defeat

Pride and Death

Nothingness

Horror

CIRCLE OF STORIES: ONE

2

FIRST STORY

BEGINNINGS

"When all things began..."

When all things began, the Word already was. The Word dwelt with God, and what God was, the Word was. The Word, then, was with God at the beginning, and through him all things came to be; no single thing was created without him. All that came to be was alive with his life, and that life was the light of men. The light shines on in the dark, and the darkness has never mastered it.

John 1, 1–5

Listen. Put on morning

. . .

Listen. Put on lightbreak.
Waken into miracle.
The audience lies awake
Under the tenements
Under the sugar docks
Under the printed moments.
The centuries turn their locks
And open under the hill
Their inherited books and doors
All gathered to distill
Like happy berry pickers
One voice to talk to us.
Yes listen. It carries away
The second and the years
Till the heart's in a jacket of snow
And the head's in a helmet of white
And the song sleeps to be wakened
By the morning ear bright.
Listen. Put on morning.
Waken into falling light.

W. S. Graham

"And God said..."

And God said, Let us make man in our image, after our likeness: and let them have dominion over the fish of the sea, and over the fowl of the air, and over the cattle, and over all the earth, and over every creeping thing that creepeth upon the earth. So God created man in his own image, in the image of God created he him; male and female created he them. And God blessed them, and God said unto them, Be fruitful, and multiply, and replenish the earth, and subdue it: and have dominion over the fish of the sea, and over the fowl of the air, and over every living thing that moveth upon the earth.

And God said, Behold, I have given you every herb-bearing seed, which is upon the face of all the earth, and every tree, in the which is the fruit of a tree yielding seed; to you it shall be for meat. And to every beast of the earth, and to every fowl of the air, and to every thing that creepeth upon the earth, wherein there is life, I have given every green herb for meat: and it was so. And God saw every thing that he had made, and, behold, it was very good. And the evening and the morning were the sixth day.

Genesis 1, 26–31

The Animals

They do not live in the world,
Are not in time and space.
From birth to death hurled
No word do they have, not one
To plant a foot upon,
Were never in any place.
For with names the world was called
Out of the empty air,
With names was built and walled,
Line and circle and square,
Dust and emerald;
Snatched from deceiving death
By the articulate breath.

But these have never trod
Twice the familiar track,
Never never turned back
Into the memoried day.
All is new and near
In the unchanging Here
Of the fifth great day of God,
That shall remain the same,
Never shall pass away.

On the sixth day we came.

Edwin Muir

Muir seems to suggest that when "we" (human beings) came, on the sixth day of creation, things began to go wrong. But he also says that creation as it was on the fifth day "Never shall pass away." Is this idea —that the first creation has lasting beauty—similar to John's idea that the light will shine on?

Kumulipo or Beginning-in-deep-darkness

"Kumulipo" or "Beginning-in-deep-darkness" is an ancient Polynesian myth about the mysterious origins of all things. It takes the form of a prayer chant.

There was a time when there was only night and darkness, darkness that gave forth black darkness, night that gave forth deeper night.

In this time the earth became hot; the heavens swirled and turned. The Pleiades rose in the night. And slime was the source of the earth.

In the night Kumulipo was born, a male, Kumulipo, the Source-of-deep-darkness; and Po'ele was born, a female, Po'ele whose name was Darkness. These were the parents of all hard-shelled things that came into being in the sea in the darkness and of all plant life. The coral was the first living creature, and the first stone. The grub came forth that digs and heaps up little mounds of dirt; and his child the earthworm was born. The starfish came forth, and his child, the little starfish, was born.

The barnacle was born, and the oyster; the mussel was born; the hermit crab came forth. The big limpet was born and his child the small limpet. The shellfish, the rock oyster, the clam, the sea snail, the conch, and the small conch child were born in the night.

Moss was born, living in the sea; ferns grew, living in the land. Earth and water were food for the plants, for the seagrass, the seaweeds, for the landgrass, for the mints which came forth from the land.

The god might enter this vast time and place, but not yet man. Darkness slipped into light, but it was still night.

The man with the water gourd was a god, Kane-i-ka-wai-ola. He gave water to the plants; the withered vine grew green. The long night was fruitful; the long night passed, but still it was night.

Pouliuli, the male, was born, Pouliuli, Deep-profound-darkness; born was the female, Powehiwehi, whose name means Darkness-streaked-with-glimmering-light. These two were parents of all the fish and creatures of the ocean.

The waters floated. The fish were born; porpoises were swimming in the sea. The child of the *hilu* fish swam and rested and spread his tail-fin. The shark swam forth and the sturgeon; the eel and the ray and the octopus were swimming here and there. The albacore, the mackerel, and the squid were born to swim in the sea water. The pickerel was living in the sea. The gourd vine, the taro, and the yam flourished on the land. Rushes abounded; the sandalwood and hibiscus lived and grew. The fish were swarming in the waters. They swam, rising, jerking, diving, each one swallowing, swallowing as he went. Dark was the ocean. It was still night.

Darkness hung over the sea and the land; darkness shadowed the streams and the mountains. Darkness still covered the dimly brightening night.

Po'el'ele, the male, was born, Po'el'ele, Dark-night; born was Pohaha, the female, whose name means Night-just-breaking-into-dawn. These two were parents of all tiny frail and flitting things which came to being in the ever-lessening light. The rootstalk sprouted nine leaves; the taro grew.

The wood-borer was born and its child was a flying thing. The caterpillar was born and its child, the moth, flew forth. The ant was born; the dragonfly flew over land and stream; the grasshopper leaped about; out came fly, the child of the worm.

The egg was born and its child was a bird: the snipe, the plover, the flycatcher, the crow came forth from the eggs and flew about. The little brown creeper flew; the curlew and its child, the stilt, were born. The frigate-bird and the albatross flew out.

The heron came into the world and flew about the seashore in great flocks and settled down on the beaches. The duck of the islands lived beside the sea; the wild duck and the goose and the owl lived on the land.

The earth was covered with young birds in the night that was just breaking into dawn. It was time for the dawn but it was still night.

Popanopano, the male, was born; born was Polalowehi, the female. This was the time when the crawlers came out of the sea and took to the land. This was the time of the egg-layers. The sea crept up upon the land, slipped back, rushed forward; the crawlers advanced and produced eggs.

So were born in the night the rough-backed turtles, the dark-red turtles, the horn-billed turtles, and the little lobsters. The slow and slippery geckos were born, and other creatures, fat and mud-dwelling, leaving tracks upon the ground, creeping and crawling and poking about.

The time came at last for Po-kanokano, the male, the Nightdigger, and Po-lalo-uli, the female, to produce.

Then in the night world the pig child, Kamapua'a, was born and went to live inland in the bush. Dark was the skin of the new generation. The nose of the beautiful black pig dug into the land and heaped it up; he cultivated the taro patches and the increase of the land was tenfold; the land sprang into bloom. The ancient line of the pig scattered and multiplied, and left their footprints in the rocks.

Po-hiolo, the male, was born, Po-hiolo, Night-falling-away; born was Po-ne'a-aku, the female, whose name meant Night-creeping-away. These were the parents of Pilo'i, the rat child. This was the time of the nibblers, brown-coated, the rats, with whiskers. They hid here and there in the world. They dug holes to live in, scratched in the wet earth. They ate in the uplands; they ate the new shoots of the taro, pilfered the fruits and nibbled the rinds. They were born in the dark, while the dark slipped away. But it was still night.

Po-ne'e-aku, the male, was born, Po-ne'e-aku, Night-receding; born was Po-neie-mai, the female, whose name meant Pregnant-night. These were the parents of a new, mysterious birth. The night grew less. The dark lightened. The dog was born, dark-red, brindled, hairless, pitiful in the cold without a coat, in the heat without cover. The wind was his companion.

Out of the slime came new rootlets; the leaves branched. Birth spread through the world. The dog was born while it was still night. But men were not far.

Po-kinikini and Po-he'enalu-mamao were parents of the next life. The night was passing and a child was born, well-formed. This was the time when men were born by the hundreds: man was born for the narrow stream; woman was born for the broad stream. They stood together; they slept together, in that calm time long ago, called Calmness. A great stillness lay about, awaiting the gods and man.

La'ila'a was born, a woman; a man was born, named Ki'i. The god was Kane. The face of the god was ruddy; dark was the face of man.

Here was the ocean edge, here the damp forests, the cold mountains. This was the time when men were born, little helpless ones, then children growing older, ever increasing.

Man spread over the land. Man was here.

It was day.

Retold by Maria Leach

In "Kumulipo" man is recognized as a child of the plants, animals, and sea creatures that first came to life in the world. He is also part of the deep darkness that existed before the world, of the slime from which the earth slowly evolved, and of the mysterious germ of life itself.

How does this story of the emergence of living things contrast with the biblical accounts you have just read?

"But it was still night." These words are said over and over again in this myth. When does light finally come? What does John (in the passage that opens this book) say about light and darkness?

The Story of Zal

With "The Story of Zal" we move from stories and
poems of creation to a Persian tale about the strange
birth and childhood of a boy who was born with the
snow-white hair of an old man.

Hundreds of years ago there lived a prince whose name was Saum.
He had an enormous palace and an army to protect his lands, but he
was under the dominion of the shah, the ruler of all Persia.

One day there was a commotion in the women's apartment of
Saum's palace. The ladies in waiting were chattering away, as ladies will,
and some of them were lamenting and shaking their heads.

"Was there ever such a misfortune?" asked one. "Was ever such a
child seen before?"

"It's a beautiful baby," said another, "strong and in the best of
health. Indeed, he would be perfect were it not—were it not—"

"There you have it," interrupted a third. "Beautiful except, perfect
except. . . . Have you heard what the princess has named him? Zal, the
aged one, and the baby scarcely a day old! But who is to tell the father?
Who is brave enough to risk his wrath when he hears that his only son
has hair as white as the mountain snows?"

The ladies looked at one another. No one felt inclined to give Prince
Saum such curious news.

"Perhaps it would be better to wait a little," said the first speaker.
"The hair may darken or it might even fall out."

So they waited a few days, but the baby's hair remained as thick
and white as ever.

"The father must be told," said the nurse, who was more courageous
and energetic than the other ladies. She went boldly into Prince Saum's
presence and threw herself upon the ground before him.

"O Prince, live forever," she said. "May I have your permission to speak?"

"Say on," replied Saum.

"The world is full of beauty, the moon and stars in the night sky, the singing birds, the flowers in the garden, but none more beautiful than your first child, your infant son. Healthy he is and strong like the elephant, and his hair—"

"A son," interrupted the prince. "Why did you not bring him here at once?"

"His hair—" repeated the nurse.

"Never mind his hair," said Saum, "fetch him."

The nurse began to rise. "Your son has the hair of the aged," she said, as she backed away from the royal presence. "His mother calls him Zal."

Saum was distressed. This was an evil omen indeed. When the baby was brought before him, he saw that the nurse had spoken the truth. The child was large and strong for his age, and his head was covered with snow-white hair.

"Call my wise men," commanded the prince. "They must help me decide what to do."

The wise men looked at the baby and shook their heads. They had never seen such a child before. "He may even be a demon," said one. "We must consult the stars."

All night they scanned the heavens and murmured together. As soon as the sun began to rise, they returned to their prince. "You must not keep this baby," they said. "Get rid of him at once or dreadful misfortunes will befall your people. Your enemies will invade the land and you will be unable to resist them."

Saum looked at the baby in sorrow. Surely it was strange to see the small face crowned with an abundance of white hair. Perhaps the child really was an evil spirit. So at last he consented, and Zal was taken far from home to a spot where Mount Alberz raises her lofty head to touch the sky. There the baby was placed on a rock and abandoned.

Mount Alberz is so high that no man has ever been able to climb to its summit; but on the topmost peak the simurgh has her nest. As she is a marvelous creature, differing from anything that flies, so her nest is a marvelous structure. It is made of ebony and sandalwood, twined with aloes, and it is kept fragrant with cedar and spices.

From her high retreat, the simurgh could look down on the surrounding countryside, and seeing that a group of men had left something on a rock, she flew from her nest to examine it. The baby was awake and wailing so piteously that the heart of the simurgh was filled with compassion at the sound. She gathered him up and carried him to her nest. There she fed him bits of fruit and morsels of meat—an unusual diet for one so young, but Zal thrived on it. As time passed, he learned to crawl about the spacious nest and he became devoted to his foster mother.

She realized that he was no ordinary child and spent much of the time teaching him. Being no ordinary creature herself, she was able to instruct him in the language of his own people so that he would be able to converse with them when the time came for him to return home. Year after year went by and Zal grew tall and handsome, but he never left the mountain except for short trips on the back of his foster mother.

No other children were born to Prince Saum, and from time to time he was sorely troubled by the recollection of the white-haired baby left to perish on the rocks. One night he had a dreadful dream in which voices taunted him, saying, "Is it truly a crime to have white hair? Look in the mirror. See what is happening to your own dark locks. O unnatural father, does this mean that you, too, are an evil spirit?"

The prince awoke, trembling with fear, and the next day he sent some of his servants to see if they could find out what had happened to the baby. The simurgh did not notice their approach, and since they did not see her, the men returned without any information. Surely a child abandoned in such a desolate place must soon have been devoured by wild beasts.

Once again Saum had a dream, and this time he thought he saw a young man with snow-white hair, riding at the head of an army. He consulted his wise men and asked them what these strange nightmares meant.

"We must consider," answered the wise men. They withdrew from his presence and murmured together for eight hours. Then they came back and said, "O Prince, live forever, your son is still alive."

"Where is he then?" asked Saum.

"That we cannot tell. But you must seek for him yourself. Go first to the place where he was abandoned."

Saum was not accustomed to traveling alone so he called out the army and they set forth, mounted on beautiful horses and carrying silken

banners that floated in the breeze. They made quite a display as they crossed the rocks at the foot of the mountain. The simurgh saw them and immediately guessed who they were.

"The time has come," she said to Zal, "for you to return to your own people."

"No, oh no," cried the boy. "This is where I belong. Why do you want to get rid of me?"

The simurgh soothed him. "I have no wish to be parted from you," she said, "but you will soon be a man and you are destined to be a famous hero. I must carry you to your father."

The boy shed tears at the thought of leaving her and begged to be allowed to stay.

"Hush, I promise that you will see me again," she assured him. Then she plucked out one of her feathers and gave it to him, saying, "If you are ever in trouble, put this feather in the fire. As soon as it burns, no matter where you are, I shall come to you." She then carried him to the place where his father was standing.

Saum saw the snow-white hair of the youth and knew at once that this must be Zal. He bowed low before the simurgh. "O wonder creature," he said, "you have preserved the life of my son. All these years you must have cherished him." But before he could finish thanking her, she stretched her great, feathered wings and flew back to the mountaintop.

Saum turned to Zal and expressed his sorrow at all that had happened. He promised to do everything in his power to make up for his wickedness. "Let us try to forget the past," he said, "and rejoice and make merry for we have much to look forward to now that we are together again."

When they returned to the palace, the whole city celebrated the homecoming of Zal, and his story was told far and wide. It even reached the ears of the shah, and he requested that the boy be brought to court. So Saum presented his son before the ruler of all Persia.

The shah was delighted with the boy's appearance, and in token of his favor he gave Zal princely garments and a number of beautiful horses. "I am astonished," he said to Saum, "that your son speaks with such fluency and behaves with such courtesy. Still you must get many tutors for him. He can hardly have learned such things as our customs of the banquet while living in a nest."

So Zal had many tutors, and so clever was he that in a short time he had learned all that was required of a prince. His father was able to entrust much of the government to him. But wherever the young man went, he carried the feather of the simurgh, not knowing when the moment might come that he would require her help.

As time passed Zal was married to a lovely lady who was known as the moon of Persia. He was devoted to her, but before their first child was born she became so sick and restless that he was very deeply concerned. He felt certain she was about to die. Surely this was the time for him to ask the aid and advice of his foster mother. He took out the feather and thrust it into the fire.

No sooner had it begun to burn than the simurgh appeared beside him. "Why do you look so sad," she asked, "when you have every reason to rejoice? Your wife is going to have a son who will be such a hero all nations will know his name. You have nothing to worry about. She will soon be well and happy."

With these words the magic creature vanished, but everything happened just as she had said it would. The baby was called Rustem, and for many generations poets sang of his glorious deeds.

In what ways is the "wonder creature" called the simurgh a better parent to Zal than his natural father is?

What kind of "beginning" does this legend tell about? In answering, you should consider the last paragraph as well as the story itself.

We can speak of two kinds of innocence. An "innocent" person could be someone who is unaware of a "scientific" explanation of life, or who deliberately ignores it. (Such a person can believe in magic and enchantment, for example.) Or, an "innocent" person is someone who has never experienced the clash between good and evil. Sometimes the two kinds of innocence go together, sometimes not. Do you see any suggestions of these kinds of innocence in "The Story of Zal" or in the creation selections that open this anthology?

What "marvelous" or supernatural elements in "The Story of Zal" let us know that it is part of a "romantic" kind of literature, not restricted to descriptions of how things actually are in the world we normally live in?

You might try to write a poem and a tale, taking what you have read here as models. The poem could, like "The Animals," take one of the new creatures at the time of creation and describe it. You should try to show a contrast between "then" (long ago) and "now" (the time we live in). You might pretend to be the animal yourself. Do not attempt rhyme. Lots of good poems do not rhyme.

Your second composition, a tale about the beginning of a heroic life and some of a hero's early adventures, should include a sense of an idealized or simplified romantic world. In other words, don't worry about making the tale believable; concentrate instead on a gripping adventure story.

INNOCENCE

Margaret

Many birds and the beating of wings
Make a flinging reckless hum
In the early morning at the rocks
Above the blue pool
Where the gray shadows swim lazy.

In your blue eyes, O reckless child,
I saw today many little wild wishes,
Eager as the great morning.

Carl Sandburg

Adam and Eve in Eden

When the Lord God made earth and heaven, there was neither shrub nor plant growing wild upon the earth, because the Lord God had sent no rain on the earth; nor was there any man to till the ground. A flood used to rise out of the earth and water all the surface of the ground. Then the Lord God formed a man from the dust of the ground and breathed into his nostrils the breath of life. Thus the man became a living creature. Then the Lord God planted a garden of Eden away to the east, and there he put the man whom he had formed. The Lord God made trees spring from the ground, all trees pleasant to look at and good for food; and in the middle of the garden he set the tree of life and the tree of the knowledge of good and evil.

There was a river flowing from Eden to water the garden, and when it left the garden it branched into four streams. The name of the first is Pishon; that is the river which encircles all the land of Havilah, where the gold is. The gold of that land is good; bdellium and cornelians are also to be found there. The name of the second river is Gihon; this is the one which encircles all the land of Cush. The name of the third is Tigris; this is the river which runs east of Asshur. The fourth river is the Euphrates.

The Lord God took the man and put him in the garden of Eden to till it and care for it. He told the man, "You may eat from every tree in the garden, but not from the tree of the knowledge of good and evil; for on the day that you eat from it, you will certainly die." Then the Lord God said, "It is not good for the man to be alone. I will provide a partner for him." So God formed out of the ground all the wild animals and all the birds of heaven. He brought them to the man to see what he would call them, and whatever the man called each living creature, that was its

name. Thus the man gave names to all cattle, to the birds of heaven, and to every wild animal; but for the man himself no partner had yet been found. And so the Lord God put the man into a trance, and while he slept, he took one of his ribs and closed the flesh over the place. The Lord God then built up the rib, which he had taken out of the man, into a woman. He brought her to the man, and the man said:
"Now this, at last—

> bone from my bones,
> flesh from my flesh!—
> this shall be called woman,
> for from man was this taken."

That is why a man leaves his father and mother and is united to his wife, and the two become one flesh. Now they were both naked, the man and his wife, but they had no feeling of shame towards one another.

Genesis 2, 5–25

The poet sees Margaret in "early morning" and he compares the wild wishes in her eyes to "the great morning." Can these "mornings" be connected in some way with the "morning" of Adam and Eve's innocent life in Eden?

Behold the Rib!

I take my text from Genesis two and twenty-one

Behold the rib!
Now, my beloved,
Behold means to look and see.
Look at this woman God done made,
But first thing, ah hah!
I want you to gaze upon God's previous works.
Almighty and arisen God, hah!
Peace-giving and prayer-hearing God,
High-riding and strong-armed God
Walking across his globe creation, hah!
With the blue elements for a helmet
And a wall of fire round his feet
He wakes the sun every morning from his fiery bed
With the breath of his smile
And commands the moon with his eyes.
And oh—
With the eye of faith
I can see him.
Even the lion had a mate,
So God shook his head
And a thousand million diamonds
Flew out from his glittering crown
And studded the evening sky and made the stars.
So God put Adam into a deep sleep
And took out a bone, ah hah!
And it is said that it was a rib.
Behold the rib!
A bone out of a man's side.
He put the man to sleep and made wo-man,

And men and women been sleeping together ever since.
Behold the rib!
Brothers, if God
Had taken that bone out of man's head
He would have meant for woman to rule, hah,
If he had taken a bone out of his foot,
He would have meant for us to dominize and rule.
He could have made her out of back-bone
And then she would have been behind us.
But, no, God Almighty, he took the bone out of his side
So that places the woman beside us;
Hah! God knew his own mind.
Behold the rib!
And now I leave this thought with you,
Standing out on the eaves of ether,
Breathing clouds from out his nostrils,
Blowing storms from 'tween his lips,
I can see!!
Him seize the mighty ax of his proving power
And smite the stubborn-standing space,
And laid it wide open in a mighty gash—
Making a place to hold the world.
I can see him—
Molding the world out of thought and power
And whirling it out on its eternal track,
Ah hah, my strong armed God!
He set the blood-red eye of the sun in the sky
And told it,
Wait, wait! Wait there till Shiloh come.
I can see!
Him mold the mighty mountains
And melting the skies into seas.
Oh, behold, and look and see! hah,
We see in the beginning
He made the beasts every one after its kind,
The birds that fly the trackless air,
The fishes that swim the mighty deep—
Male and fee-male, hah!
Then he took of the dust of the earth
And made man in his own image.
And man was alone.

Let us all go marchin' up to the gates of glory.
Tramp! tramp! tramp!
In step with the host that John saw.
Male and female, like God made us,
Side by side.
Oh, behold the rib!
And let's all sit down in glory together
Right 'round his glorified throne
And praise his name forever.

AMEN

What "previous works" of creation are described in this sermon, before the image of the rib becomes central? How do they prepare you for the story of woman's creation? How does the preacher-poet explain the significance of the rib?

Is there anything in this sermon that undercuts, or lessens, the sense of the glory of God and of the first man and woman?

To the Wild Cows

In all the years that we lived in Warsaw, I never left the city. Other boys used to talk about their vacations. People went out to Falencia, to Miedzeszyn, Michalin, Swider, Otwock—but for me these were only names. No trees grew on Krochmalna Street. Near No. 24, where I went to cheder, there was a tree, but No. 24 was far from our house.

Some of the neighbors had potted flowers, but my parents considered this a pagan custom. I, however, had an inborn love of nature. In the summertime I would sometimes find a leaf still attached to the stem of an apple, and such a leaf would arouse both joy and longing in me. I would sniff at it and carry it around with me until it withered. Mother brought home a bunch of carrots, parsley, red radishes, cucumbers—and every vegetable reminded me of the days in Radzymin, where I had been surrounded by fields and orchards. Once I found a whole ear of corn in my straw mattress. This ear of corn awakened many memories. Among other things it reminded me of the dream of Pharaoh, wherein the seven lean ears of corn devoured the seven fat ones.

Many different kinds of flies used to alight on the railing of our balcony: large, small, dark, green-gold. When a butterfly would stray there, I would not try to catch it, but would hold my breath and stare in wonder. The little fluttering creature was for me a greeting from the world of freedom.

But Mother Nature did her work even on Krochmalna Street. In the winter the snow fell, in the summer the rains came. High over the rooftops the clouds passed—dark ones, light ones, some like silver, some in the shapes of fish, snakes, sheep, brooms. Occasionally hail fell on our balcony, and once, after the rain, a rainbow stretched above the roofs. Father told me to recite the blessing "Who remembereth the Covenant."

At night the moon shone and the stars appeared. It was all a great mystery.

My friend Boruch-Dovid was always talking about the fields and wastelands that lie beyond Warsaw, and about the wild cows that graze there. I began to demand that he take me there. He delayed as long as he could and put me off with various excuses. But finally it reached the point where he had to make good on his promises or our friendship would end.

One Friday in the summertime I arose very early, so early that the sky was still glowing from the sunrise. To my mother I made some pretext or other, put a few slices of bread and butter in a paper bag, took from its hiding place a kopeck I had somehow saved from my allowance, and went off to meet Boruch-Dovid. I had never been up so early in the morning, and everything looked cooler, fresher, and somehow like a fairy-tale landscape. Here and there a stone was damp and Boruch-Dovid said it was because of the dew. This meant, then, that there was dew even on Krochmalna Street. I had thought that dew fell only in the Land of Israel. . . .

Not only the street, but the people too looked fresher. I discovered that early in the morning various farm wagons came to our street. Gentiles from the surrounding villages brought vegetables, chickens, geese, ducks, and freshly laid chicken eggs (not the lime-preserved eggs one could buy in Zelda's shop). On Mirowski Street, behind the market halls, was the wholesale fruit market. The abundance of all the orchards around Warsaw was brought here: apples, pears, cherries, sour cherries, gooseberries, currants. Here too were traded strange fruits and vegetables that most Jewish children had never tasted and thought forbidden: tomatoes, cauliflowers, green peppers. Inside the market halls proper, one could get pomegranates and bananas. These were bought only by grand ladies, whose shopping baskets were carried by servant girls.

Boruch-Dovid and I walked quickly. As we walked, he told many strange tales. His father, he said, had gone on foot from Warsaw to Skierniewice and on the way he had met a wild man. I was very curious about the appearance of the wild man and Boruch-Dovid gave me a detailed description: tall, with scales instead of skin, long hair reaching to the ground, and a horn growing in the middle of his forehead. For breakfast such a creature always ate a live child. I was panic-stricken and I asked, "Maybe a wild man will attack us?"

"No, they are far from Warsaw."

I should not have been so gullible. But I always believed everything Boruch-Dovid told me.

We passed through Nalewki and Muranow Streets, and from there the road led to the open country. I saw broad meadows covered with grass and all sorts of flowers, and mountains of a kind I had never known to exist. At the top they were indeed mountains, but at the bottom there were brick walls with small, sunken windows covered by iron grates.

"What is that?" I asked.

"The Citadel."

A feeling of dread came over me. I had heard of the Citadel. Here were imprisoned those who had tried to overthrow the Tsar.

I had not yet seen any wild cows, but what I had seen already was wonderful and strange. The sky here was not a narrow strip as on Krochmalna Street, but broad, spread out like the ocean, and it descended to the earth like a heavenly curtain. Birds flew overhead in swarms, with a twittering, a cawing, a whistling—large birds and small birds. Two storks were circling above one of the hills of the Citadel. Butterflies of all colors fluttered above the grass: white, yellow, brown, with all kinds of dots and patterns. The air smelled of earth, of grass, of the smoke of locomotives, and of something more that intoxicated me and made my head reel. There was a strange stillness here, and yet everything murmured, rustled, chirped. Blossoms fell from somewhere and settled on the lapels of my coat. I looked up at the sky, saw the sun, the clouds, and suddenly I understood more clearly the meaning of the words of Genesis. This, then, was the world God had created: the earth, the heavens, the waters above that are separated by the firmament from the waters below.

Boruch-Dovid and I climbed up a hill and below us we saw the Vistula. One half glittered like silver, the other half was green as gall. A white ship sailed past. The river itself did not stand still—it flowed, it was headed somewhere, with an eagerness that hinted at miracles and the coming of the Messiah.

"That's the Vistula," explained Boruch-Dovid. "It flows all the way to Danzig."

"And then?"

"Then it flows into the sea."

"And where is the Leviathan?"

"Far away, at the end of the earth."

Then the storybooks did not tell lies, after all. The world *is* filled with wonders. One need merely pass through Muranow Street and one street more, and already one was in the midst of marvels. The end of the earth? Was not *this* the end of the earth? . . .

Locomotives whistled, but no trains could be seen. Gentle breezes were blowing, and each brought with it a different fragrance—aromas long forgotten or never dreamed of. A honeybee came from somewhere, alit on a flower, smelled at it, hummed, and flew on to the next flower. Boruch-Dovid said, "She wants to collect honey."

"Can she bite?"

"Yes, and she has a special poison."

He, Boruch-Dovid, knows everything. If I were alone, I could not find my way home. Already I have forgotten even the direction toward Warsaw. But he is as much at home here as in his own courtyard. Suddenly he starts to run. He pretends to run away from me. He throws himself down and is hidden by the tall grass. Boruch-Dovid is gone! I am alone in the world—a lost child, just like in the storybooks.

"Boruch-Dovid!" I began to call. "Boruch-Dovid!"

I call, but my voice rebounds from somewhere. There is an echo here, as in a synagogue, but it is thrown back from a great distance and the voice is changed and terrifying.

"Boruch-Dovid! Boruch-Dovid! . . ."

I know that he is only playing a joke on me. He wants to frighten me. But though I know it, I am afraid. My voice is breaking with sobs.

"Bo-r-uch Do-v-id! . . ."

He reappears, his black eyes laughing like a gypsy's, and begins to run about in circles like a young colt. His coattails fly. His fringed vest billows in the wind. He too has become like a wild creature in the lap of nature.

"Come on, let's go to the Vistula!"

The path leads downhill, and we cannot walk—we run. Our feet seem to be running by themselves. I have to hold mine back so they won't run even faster and jump right into the water. But the water is farther away than I had thought. As I run, the river becomes broader, like an ocean. We come to dunes of pebbles and moist sand, long and marked with lines, like giant cakes made by children playing in the sand. Boruch-Dovid takes off his boots, rolls up his pants legs, and wades into the water up to his ankles.

"Ouch, it's cold!"

He tells me to take off my boots. But I am embarrassed. Walking barefoot is not in my nature. Only rowdies and Gentile boys go barefoot.

"Are there any fish here?"

"Yes, lots of fish."

"Do they bite?"

"Sometimes."

"What will you do if a fish bites you?"

"I'll grab it by the tail . . ."

Compared to me, Boruch-Dovid is a country boy, a peasant. I sit down on a rock and everything inside me flows, gurgles like the waters of the Vistula. My mind sways with the motion of the waves and it seems to me that not only the Vistula, but everything around me—the hills, the sky, I myself—is swaying, flowing away into the distance, toward Danzig. Boruch-Dovid points to the other shore and says, "Over there is the Praga forest."

This means that near me there is a real forest, full of wild animals and robbers.

Suddenly something extraordinary happens. From the left, where the sky and the waters meet, something comes floating on the water, but it is not a ship. At first it seems small, enveloped in a haze. Soon it grows larger and more distinct. It is a group of rafts made of logs. Men lean against long poles and push them with all the weight of their bodies. On one of the rafts there is a little hut—a small house out on the water! Even Boruch-Dovid stares in open-mouthed wonder.

It takes a long, long time for the rafts to come close to us. The men yell something to us. I notice someone who looks like a Jew. He has a beard. I think I can even make out a Jewish skullcap. From my reading of the parables of the Preacher of Dubnow, I know that Jewish merchants make voyages to Danzig and Leipzig. I have even heard that timber is shipped by water. But now I see it with my own eyes—a tale of the Dubnow preacher brought to life! For a while the rafts are near us. A dog stands at the edge of one of them and barks directly at us. Woe to us, if he could jump across the water! He would tear us to shreds. After a while, the rafts move on. Time has passed, the sun has already reached the middle of the sky and is now moving into the west. Only after the rafts have disappeared beneath a bridge do we start to go back, not the way we came, but in a different direction.

I remember the wild cows and am about to ask Boruch-Dovid where they are, but I don't. I suddenly realize that the wild cows and the wild man are nothing but his imagination. We would never encounter any of them. As a matter of fact, when I had told my mother about the wild cows she had asked, "If there are such cows, why don't they catch them and sell them to the dairies? And how is it possible that they have only been seen by your friend Boruch-Dovid?" She was just as skeptical about the wild cows as she had been about the shrieking geese.

The sun is reddening. At home Mother is surely beginning to worry —she is so nervous. Soon it will be time to take the Sabbath stew to the baker, and who will be there to carry it? We begin to walk quickly, each sunk in his own thoughts, while above our heads the birds play, and the windows of the Citadel glow red and gold in the sunset.

I think of those who lie inside in chains because they tried to over-throw the Tsar. I seem to see their eyes, and suddenly everything is filled with a Sabbath Eve sadness and eeriness.

Isaac Bashevis Singer

List the ways in which the boy in this autobiographical account relates his experience of a new, wild freedom to the literature he has read. Does this story suggest that the boy's experience in the country has prepared him for something?

This is a real boy whose world is strongly affected by the many tales that had been told to him. What elements of romance in the boy's world undergo a change in the story?

"I was made
for battle..."

Ages ago, the Norsemen said, there was a time when heaven, earth, and sea did not exist. In all the universe there was nothing but a region of boiling flame and a region of cold with a great gap lying between. Rivers of ice pushed out into this gap, and the red heat of the fires from the other side beat fiercely upon them. Steam arose, and the whole space was filled with swirling mist.

At last these clouds took shape, and out of them Ymer, the first frost giant, was born. Next, the shifting particles formed a great cow, by whose milk Ymer was nourished. Thereupon he grew greatly in vigor, and his vague outline became clear and firm. In this way the frost giant was given life, and in time sons and daughters were born to him out of the mist.

In the meantime the cow who had nurtured the frost giant found no nourishment herself. Eventually she began to lick at the ice blocks which were pushed out of the region of cold. As the ice melted under her rough tongue, it shaped itself into the outline of a huge head. The cow licked further, and features became distinct. She licked again, and blue eyes opened. At last this other huge creature was formed, and he rose up and looked at the misty gap in which the vast shapes of the frost giants could be vaguely seen.

This being was Bure, who was ancestor of the gods, and great power was in him. The moment he beheld the frost giants, he knew they were evil and resolved to destroy them. He cried aloud upon his son and his grandsons who were yet unborn, until the whole gap thundered and rolled with the echoes of his mighty voice. Out of his warm breath and the power of his magic, his descendants were born. Then the gods lifted up their arms and rushed against the frost giants. The mists of the gap swirled in confusion as the two races battled in their midst.

Bure was slain in the mighty struggle, but the gods destroyed Ymer

at last and routed their enemies. The remaining frost giants fled into the outer regions of the great gap, where they made themselves a land of mountains and mist to dwell in.

As the thunder of combat died away, Bure's grandson, Allfather Odin, looked down on Ymer's vast body which sprawled across the center of the gap. "The frost giant was made out of mist," said he, "and his form is still fluid. Let us shape it anew into a world for us all to dwell in."

The other gods gladly agreed. "Ymer's body shall be earth," they declared, and they formed it into land, round and flat like a wheel. In the center they piled mountains, for there they planned to build Asgard, which was to be their home and strong citadel. Next they took Ymer's misty skull for the great arch of heaven. They changed his blood into blue ocean water, which they poured around the outer edge of the earth as a barrier between themselves and Giantland. They stole sparks from the fiery regions to light the stars, and built chariots in which they set sun and moon spirits to ride over the earth.

In this way the world was created, but though Ymer was dead, his body was divine, and life of a kind was still in it. Grass began to grow on the earth. Forests sprang up and animals appeared. "We must make rulers for these things," said Odin at last. "Let us shape beings like ourselves who shall watch over the earth and make it prosper."

Under the ground and on the earth's surface small, creeping things had come to life. The gods made these like themselves, and in this way the light elves and dark dwarfs were born. Neither race pleased the gods entirely. The dwarfs were wonderful craftsmen, but their nature was evil, and they fled into the caverns of the earth to live in darkness out of sight of the gods. The elves blessed the animals and crops, but they built their own home of Elfland up in the air.

"These races are not truly our creation," said Odin. "They had life of themselves, and we only gave them shape. Let us make a new master on earth." This time the gods took trees from the forest, breathed life into them, and formed them into Woman and Man.

Men and women looked to the gods for protection, but the power of the gods was limited. Many things appeared in the world which were not created by the gods and opposed them. Beyond earth there still dwelt the frost giants. Hel, the monstrous daughter of a god and a giantess, built a kingdom of darkness under the earth, where she ruled over the spirits of the dead. The great world serpent encircled the earth at the bottom of the sea. Dark wolves pursued the chariots of the terrified sun and moon. Far above the earth, demons were born in the regions of boiling fire. All these great forces of evil threatened the world, and none knew whether they or the gods would prevail.

Odin was the master of the gods, and he was infinitely wise, for he had paid with the sight of one keen, blue eye for a drink from the waters of wisdom. It now seemed to him time to talk to the maidens in whose hands the future lay. These were the Norns, or Fates, some of whom were said to be elves, some dwarfs. In any case, they lived in the heavens near the upper end of the rainbow, which was the bridge between sky and earth.

The Norns sat by a many-colored fountain whose spray rose behind them like a rainbow in the air. The veils before their faces were thick and mysterious as clouds stirring and twisting in the wind. It seemed as though these would blow aside and reveal the face of the future, yet behind each fold lay always another, for none could pierce the mystery of the Norns.

"Greeting to you, Odin, Allfather," said the eldest slowly. "Greeting, Creator of the earth, and Ruler until the Day of Doom."

Odin leaned on his spear and stood watching, while wind blew out his sky-blue mantle and fluttered his white cloud of hair. "Tell me of the Day of Doom," he said at last. "How long shall my rule endure?"

The hand of the Norn was yellow and old. She raised it to draw her veil closer. "Ages of human lives," was all she said.

"How shall I fall?"

"In battle."

"Tell me what shall happen on that day."

"All evil shall assemble against you," answered the slow, deep voice of the Norn. "The serpent shall arise from the ocean with poison dripping from his jaws. The wolves of evil and darkness will come ravening to the fray. Heimdall, your watchman, shall trumpet his warning as fire demons pour down from above across the rainbow bridge. The giants will wade the ocean to battle. Hel shall arise from the land of the dead."

"Who will fight on my side?" demanded Odin.

"The spirits of the mighty dead," said she. "You will choose Valkyries, warrior maidens, and mount them on horses of cloud to ride over the battlefields of men. They will snatch up the souls of dying heroes and carry them to Valhalla, your lofty, shield-roofed hall. There they shall feast and practice their weapons, for they are to be your army in the battles of the Day of Doom."

"If I must perish on that day," said Allfather Odin, "tell me at least what shall endure."

"Nothing that now exists," said the aged Norn. "Thor, your mighty son, shall be slain by the serpent. Bright Frey will be destroyed by the fire spirits. Earth shall be burned to ashes. Wolves shall swallow the sun and moon."

"All then will be lost."

"No, not all," she answered. "Sons of your sons shall survive, and though you fall, the giants and the demons shall be utterly destroyed. Then the new race of gods will make a new, pure heaven and earth, from which all evil will have passed away."

The old Norn lifted her hand once more to her veil. Through it Odin gazed deep into sunken eyes blue and piercing as his own. "That is good," he said slowly. "I was made for battle, and mine will be the age of the fighter. Let other gods rule when the struggle is over. I will ride the howling tempest and perish in the last great storm."

The Norn turned away with a slow movement, but Odin looked long at her, her companions, and the shifting colors of the water behind. "Asgard, our citadel, is on earth," he said at last. "Here, near the wise ones, our judgment seat shall be. We will set Heimdall, our watchman, to guard the rainbow bridge, over which we will mount daily to heaven and give laws for the ruling of the world."

Retold by Olivia Coolidge

How does this myth explain the nature of evil in the world?

We said earlier that an innocent person could be someone who ignores a "scientific" explanation for life, or someone who lacks personal experience of the clash between good and evil. Look back over the five selections in this phase and define what it is in each one that makes the principal characters innocent.

THE QUEST

Merlin

Merlin was a prophet and magician in medieval stories.
In the following poem, the artist asks him if there ever will
be a runner who will break out of time and get back
to Eden, so that the apple can be hung back on the tree.

O Merlin in your crystal cave
Deep in the diamond of the day,
Will there ever be a singer
Whose music will smooth away
The furrow drawn by Adam's finger
Across the meadow and the wave?
Or a runner who'll outrun
Man's long shadow driving on,
Break through the gate of memory
And hang the apple on the tree?
Will your magic ever show
The sleeping bride shut in her bower,
The day wreathed in its mound of snow
And Time locked in his tower?

Edwin Muir

What is sought or quested for by the speaker in this poem?

What do you think the furrow drawn by Adam's finger is? Why would
the poet want the apple hung back on the tree? Who is the sleeping
bride? The poet sees "time" as having been locked in a tower. What
event would have caused this to happen? Does Muir suggest that all
human history is less perfect or desirable than the life in Eden?

The Hoard

When the moon was new and the sun young
of silver and gold the gods sung:
in the green grass they silver spilled,
and the white waters they with gold filled.
Ere the pit was dug or Hell yawned,
ere dwarf was bred or dragon spawned,
there were Elves of old, and strong spells
under green hills in hollow dells
they sang as they wrought many fair things,
and the bright crowns of the Elf-kings.
But their doom fell, and their song waned,
by iron hewn and by steel chained.
Greed that sang not, nor with mouth smiled,
in dark holes their wealth piled,
graven silver and carven gold:
over Elvenhome the shadow rolled.

There was an old dwarf in a dark cave,
to silver and gold his fingers clave;
with hammer and tongs and anvil-stone
he worked his hands to the hard bone,
and coins he made, and strings of rings,
and thought to buy the power of kings.
But his eyes grew dim and his ears dull
and the skin yellow on his old skull;
through his bony claw with a pale sheen
the stony jewels slipped unseen.
No feet he heard, though the earth quaked,
when the young dragon his thirst slaked,
and the stream smoked at his dark door.
The flames hissed on the dank floor,
and he died alone in the red fire;
his bones were ashes in the hot mire.

There was an old dragon under a gray stone;
his red eyes blinked as he lay alone.
His joy was dead and his youth spent,
he was knobbed and wrinkled, and his limbs bent
in the long years to his gold chained;
in his heart's furnace the fire waned.
To his belly's slime gems stuck thick,
silver and gold he would snuff and lick:
he knew the place of the least ring
beneath the shadow of his black wing.
Of thieves he thought on his hard bed,
and dreamed that on their flesh he fed,
their bones crushed, and their blood drank:
his ears drooped and his breath sank.
Mail-rings rang. He heard them not.
A voice echoed in his deep grot:
a young warrior with a bright sword
called him forth to defend his hoard.
His teeth were knives, and of horn his hide,
but iron tore him, and his flame died.

There was an old king on a high throne:
his white beard lay on knees of bone;
his mouth savored neither meat nor drink,
nor his ears song; he could only think
of his huge chest with carven lid
where pale gems and gold lay hid
in secret treasury in the dark ground;
its strong doors were iron-bound.
The swords of his thanes were dull with rust,
his glory fallen, his rule unjust,
his halls hollow, and his bowers cold,
but king he was of elvish gold.

J. R. R. Tolkien

This is a poem about two ages in the experience of the world: first, when "the moon was new and the sun young," and then later when nothing seemed to exist except greed and injustice. It is also about hoarded gold and the three beings who jealously guard this gold. In what way does the poem make clear that the three hoarders are essentially the same kind of being?

Is there anything in "The Hoard" to suggest that the old king whose glory has fallen may be the same person as the young warrior of stanza three?

"O strong of heart..."

O strong of heart, go where the road
Of ancient honor climbs.
Bow not your craven shoulders.
Earth conquered gives the stars.

Boethius

Compare the quest advised here with what is sought or desired in
"Merlin" and in "The Hoard."

The Song of Wandering Aengus

I went out to the hazel wood,
Because a fire was in my head,
And cut and peeled a hazel wand,
And hooked a berry to a thread;
And when white moths were on the wing,
And moth-like stars were flickering out,
I dropped the berry in a stream,
And caught a little silver trout.

When I had laid it on the floor
I went to blow the fire aflame,
But something rustled on the floor,
And someone called me by my name;
It had become a glimmering girl
With apple blossom in her hair
Who called me by my name and ran
And faded through the brightening air.

Though I am old with wandering
Through hollow lands and hilly lands,
I will find out where she has gone,
And kiss her lips and take her hands;
And walk among long dappled grass,
And pluck till time and times are done
The silver apples of the moon,
The golden apples of the sun.

William Butler Yeats

The Red Son

I love your faces I saw the many years
I drank your milk and filled my mouth
With your home talk, slept in your house
And was one of you.
            But a fire burns in my heart.
Under the ribs where pulses thud
And flitting between bones of skull
Is the push, the endless mysterious command,
            Saying:

"I leave you behind—
You for the little hills and the years all alike,
You with your patient cows and old houses
Protected from the rain,
I am going away and I never come back to you;
Crags and high rough places call me,
Great places of death
Where men go empty handed
And pass over smiling
To the star-drift on the horizon rim.
My last whisper shall be alone, unknown;
I shall go to the city and fight against it,
And make it give me passwords
Of luck and love, women worth dying for,
And money.
            I go where you wist not of
            Nor I nor any man nor woman.
            I only know I go to storms
            Grappling against things wet and naked."

There is no pity of it and no blame.
None of us is in the wrong.
After all it is only this:
> **You for the little hills and I go away.**

Carl Sandburg

Aengus says a fire was in his head and the Red Son speaks of a fire burning in his heart. Each one is driven by his desire to win certain specific goals and also something less well-defined. What are the objects of their desire?

Both Aengus and the Red Son say that their quests will take them on journeys. How are the journeys described?

Bronzeville Man with a

Belt in the Back

In such an armor he may rise and raid
The dark cave after midnight, unafraid,
And slice the shadows with his able sword
Of good broad nonchalance, hashing them down.

And come out and accept the gasping crowd,
Shake off the praises with an airiness.
And, searching, see love shining in an eye,
But never smile.

In such an armor he cannot be slain.

Gwendolyn Brooks

The Bronzeville man is a black prizefighter who fights two kinds of battle. The fight in the ring is not as important as the one after midnight when the first is finished. What do you think it is that drives the Bronzeville man to raid the "dark cave after midnight"? What *are* his sword and armor?

How Finn Won His Father's Place

In the following ancient tale we see the Irish hero Finn, as he returns from exile to save a kingdom and claim his birthright.

Now, when he left his Druid master beside the Boyne, Finn knew that the time was fully come for him to be claiming his father's place, and he set out for Tara of the High Kings.

It was Samhein, the time of the great autumn feast, and as he drew nearer, his road, and the four other roads that met at Tara, became more and more densely thronged with chiefs and warriors, on horseback or in chariots decorated with bronze and walrus ivory, with their women in gowns of green and saffron and crimson and heather-dark plaid and the golden apples swinging from the ends of their braided hair, and their tall feather-heeled hounds running alongside. For at Samhein all the kings and chiefs of Erin came together, and all men were free to sit at table in the High King's hall if they could find room—and so long as they left their weapons outside.

So up the Royal Hill and in through the gate, and across the broad forecourt went Finn, amid the incoming throng, and sat himself down with the King's household warriors, ate badger's meat baked with salt and honey, and drank the yellow mead from a silver-bound oxhorn, and watched the High King and the tall scarred man close beside him, who he knew from his lack of an eye must be Goll Mac Morna, and waited for the King to notice that there was a stranger among his warriors.

And presently the High King did notice him, and sent one of his court officials to bid him come and stand before the High Table.

"What is your name? And why do you come and seat yourself un-announced among my household warriors?" demanded the King.

And Finn flung up his pale bright head and gave him back stare for stare. "I am Finn the son of Cool who was once Captain of all the Fianna of Erin, Cormac High King, and I am come to carry my spear in your service as he did; but for me, I will carry it in the ranks of your house-hold warriors, and not with the Fianna." This he said because he knew that to join the Fianna he would have to swear faith to Goll Mac Morna, and he was no light faithbreaker.

"If you are the son of Cool, then you may be proud of your birth," said the King. "Your father was a mighty hero, and his spear I trusted as I would trust my own—and as I will trust yours."

Then Finn swore faith to Cormac the High King; and Cormac gave him a place among his household warriors, and the feasting went on as it had done before, and the King's harper beat upon his curved harp while the mead horns passed from hand to hand, and the great hounds fought over the bones among the rushes on the floor.

But little by little the drink began to pass more slowly, the laughter grew fitful and the harp-song fell away, and men began to half glance into each other's eyes and break off the glance quickly, as though afraid of what they might see.

And indeed they had good reason.

Every Samhein for the past twenty years, Tara had been weirdly and terribly visited. Fiend or Fairy, no one knew what the strange-comer was, only that his name was Aillen of the Flaming Breath, and that every Samhein at midnight he came upon them from the Fairy hill close by, and burned the royal dun over their heads. No use for any warrior, how-ever valiant, to try to withstand him, for he carried a silver harp, and as he came he drew from its strings the sweetest and most drowsy music that ever breathed upon the ears of men, and all who heard it drifted into a deep enchanted sleep. So each Samhein it was the same; he came upon Tara with no one left awake to withstand him, and he breathed where he would with a licking breath of fire until thatch and timber blackened and scorched and twisted, and kindled into leaping flame. So every year Tara must be rebuilt, and every year again—and yet again.

When the sounds of feasting had died quite away, and an uneasy hush with little stirrings and little eddies in it held the King's hall, Cor-mac rose in his High Place, and offered a mighty reward in gold and horses and women slaves to any warrior who could prevail against Aillen of the Flaming Breath, and keep the thatch on Tara till the next day's dawn. He had made the same offer, and his father before him, twenty Samhein nights, and after the first few times, no man, not the boldest of his warriors, had come forward in answer, for they knew that neither courage nor skill nor strength would avail them against the wicked silvery music. So Cormac made the offer, and waited, without hope.

And then Finn rose in his place, and stood to face the troubled King. "Cormac Mac Art, High King of Erin, I will forgo the gold and the horses and the women slaves, but if I prevail against this horror of the night, and keep the thatch on Tara till tomorrow's dawn, will you swear before all these in your hall to give me my rightful heritage?"

"It is a bold man, I'm thinking, who seeks to bargain with the High King," said Cormac. "What heritage is that?"

"The Captaincy of the Fianna of Erin."

"I have given you the place that you asked for among my own warriors," said Cormac, "and is that not good enough for you?"

"Not if I keep the thatch on Tara," said Finn.

Then a murmur ran round the hall, and men looked at each other and at Goll Mac Morna, who sat looking straight before him with his one bright falcon's eye.

"I swear," said the King, "and let all those gathered here, the kings and chiefs of Erin, warriors of my household and of all the Fianna, witness to my swearing. If you overcome Aillen of the Flaming Breath, you will have earned the Captaincy in your own right, and in your own right, as well as by heritage, you shall hold it."

So Finn left the King's hall, and took up his spear that he had laid by when he entered, and went up to the rampart walk that crested the encircling turf wall. He did not know at all how he should succeed when so many had failed before him, but his faith was in his destiny, and he did not doubt that he would prevail. And while he paced to and fro, waiting and watching, and listening more than all, one of the older warriors came after him, carrying a spear with its head laced into a leather sheath.

"Long ago your father saved my life," said the man, "and now is the time to be repaying my debt. Take the spear, to aid you in your fight."

"I have a good spear of my own," Finn said.

But the other shook his head. "Not such a spear as this, that must be kept hooded like a hawk lest it run wild and drink blood of its own ac-

51

54

cord. It was forged by Lein, the Smith of the Gods, and he beat into it the fire of the sun and the potency of the moon. When you hear the first breath of the fairy music, lay the blade to your forehead, and the fierceness and the bloodlust in it will drive away all sleep from you. Take it."

Finn took the spear and loosed the thongs and slipped off the cover. He saw a spearhead of iron as sheeny-blue as the moonlight, and studded with thirty rivets of bright Arabian gold.

"Take it," said the man once more.

And Finn hooded the spear again, but left the thongs loose. And carrying it, he returned to his pacing up and down, looking always out over the plains of Mide, white under the moon, and listening, listening until the silence in his own ears sounded loud as the hushing of the sea in a shell.

And then it came, the faintest gossamer shimmer of distant harp-music. Nearer and clearer, even as he checked to listen, clearer and nearer; the fairy music lapped like the first gentle wavelets of sleep about him. It was the light summer wind through the moorland grasses of Slieve Bloom, it was the murmur of bees among the sun-warmed bell heather; it was all the lullabies that ever his foster mothers had sung to him when he was too young to remember. . . .

Finn tore himself free of the enchantment that was weaving itself around him, and with fingers that seemed weak and numb, dragged the leather hood from the spear and pressed the blade to his forehead. Instantly he heard the voice of the spear more clearly than the voice of Aillen's harp; an angry hornet note that drove all sleep away from him. His head cleared, and looking out once more toward the Fairy hill, he saw a thing like a mist-wraith floating toward him along the ground. Nearer and nearer, taking shape and substance as it came, until Finn was looking at the pale airy shape of Aillen of the Flaming Breath, so near and clear now that he could even catch the silver ripple of the harpstrings on which the thing played with long white fingers as he came. Now Aillen had reached the stockade which crowned the turf walls, and a long tongue of greenish flame shot from his mouth and lapped at the timbers.

Finn tore off his mantle of saffron-dyed ram skins, and with one sweep of it, beat the flame into the ground.

With his flame beaten out, Aillen gave a terrible wailing cry, and turned over and back, streaming through himself like a wave flung back by a rocky shore, and fled away toward the Fairy hill. But Finn, with the hornet-shouting of the spear loud and urgent in his ears, leapt the stockade and was after him, as swift as he.

The doorway of the Fairy hill stood open, letting out a green twilight, and as Aillen fled wailing toward it, Finn made one mighty cast with the spear, and the spear flew on its way rejoicing, and passed through the creature's body and out at the other side. And there on the threshold of the Fairy hill—or where the threshold had been, for now the door was gone, and only the frost-crisped grass and brambles gleamed faintly under the moon—Aillen of the Flaming Breath lay dead, like a heap of thistledown and touchwood and the fungus that grows on the north side of trees, tangled together into somewhat the shape of a man.

Then Finn cut off the head and set it on the point of his spear and carried it back to Tara and set it up on the walls for all to see.

When morning came, and Tara still stood as it had stood last night, all men knew that Finn must have prevailed against Aillen of the Flaming Breath, and led by the High King they went out to the ramparts; and there they found Finn leaning wearily on the stockade and waiting for their coming, and nothing to show for the happenings of the night but the scorch marks on his saffron cloak which he had wrapped close about himself against the dawn chill, and the strange and ghastly head upreared on his spear point against the morning sky.

"I have kept the thatch on Tara," Finn said.

Then Cormac Mac Art set his arm across the young man's shoulders, and turned with him to face the mighty gathering in the forecourt below. "Chiefs and kings and warriors, last night ye bore witness when I swore in the mead hall that if this Finn son of Cool should prevail against Aillen of the Flaming Breath, I would set him in his father's place as Captain of the Fianna of Erin. Last night it was in my mind that it was small chance he had, where so many had failed before. But he has prevailed; he has slain the fire fiend and saved Tara, and therefore I give him to you of the Fianna for your Captain, according to my word and yours. Any of you that will not serve under him, let you leave Erin, freely and without disgrace; there are other war bands and kings' bodyguards overseas in other lands." He turned to the tall one-eyed man who stood out before the rest. "That is for you also, Goll Mac Morna, for you who have been the Fian Captain these eighteen years past. Will you strike hands with Finn Mac Cool, and lead the Connacht Fianna under him? Or will you cross the sea and carry your sword into the service of another king?"

"I will strike hands with Finn the son of Cool my old enemy," said Goll Mac Morna, though the words stuck a little in his throat, and he and Finn spat in their palms and struck hands like two men sealing a bargain.

No man went out from the High King's forecourt to carry his sword overseas, and the feud between Clan Morna and Clan Bascna, though it was not healed, was skinned over and remained so for many years to come.

So Finn Mac Cool became Captain of the Fianna of Erin, as his father had been before him.

Retold by Rosemary Sutcliff

What elements of the supernatural and the marvelous tell you that this tale, like "The Story of Zal," is a romantic one, not restricted to depicting a realistic world?

The Kamiah Monster

In their myths, North American Indians often use a character named Coyote, a godlike animal with human intelligence and ways.

Coyote was far from home, in the Buffalo country, when Blue Racer suddenly appeared before him. This was a snake, so tireless and swift that he was often used to carry important news. The very sight of this messenger brought Coyote to his feet.

"What news do you bring, Blue Racer?" he asked the snake quickly.

"Coyote!" whispered the snake, in a spent voice, and his eyes bulged, and his shining sides were dull. "Never go home, Coyote!" he warned. "As you value your life, stay here in the East forever."

"What are you saying?" snapped Coyote. "Why should I do that?"

"They are gone, all the animals, swallowed up, sucked in on the breath of the Monster."

"What Monster, Blue Racer? What are you trying to say?"

"A Monster from the sky has fallen into the Kamiah Valley, and he fills it from rim to rim. His hot breath scorches the trees and the grass, and he sucks in living things with every breath."

"Not the big things, certainly?" asked Coyote. "Mice, you mean, and rabbits, and chipmunks? Not Fox? Not Wolf? And never Bear?"

Blue Racer bent his head. "He's swallowed them, every one."

"How about yourself? Why hasn't he swallowed you?"

"I'm small and swift. I hid myself in the grass and slipped away. But heed my words, Coyote. You would not escape."

With that he was gone, and he left Coyote feeling badly shaken. But what was he to do? Stay in the East and never see a friend? It would be better to take his chances with the rest.

Coyote started bravely off, but the echo of the snake's words checked him. A Monster that filled the valley from rim to rim! He stopped, undecided.

Finally he summoned Meadowlark, and said to her, "Advise me!"

"Go you must," Meadowlark told him. "You are the only one that is left, and you must save your people. Take a bundle of pitch and five sharp flint knives, and keep your wits about you."

So Coyote sharpened five flint knives, and on the way home he gathered a bundle of pitch pine, which burns fast and hot. As he started down the river he felt the first burning breath of the Monster. At last he climbed a tree at the top of a mountain and looked off toward the Kamiah Valley. But he could see nothing because of the range of mountains that lay between. Using his cherry stick from Walla-Walla, he hit the range of mountains and made a pass.

Then he saw the Monster.

From ridge to ridge the creature stretched, spanning the whole of the valley. The sun struck sparks from its burnished scales as it stirred its tail in sleep. Then it yawned. There was a hot gust as the huge red maw came open—a terrifying sight. Quick as a flash, Coyote scrambled down the tree. He bound himself to the trunk with several stout strands of grapevine, and lay on the side of the hill in the tall grass. Using his magic to speak in a mighty voice, he called out and woke the Monster.

"Ho, there, Monster!" called Coyote. "What are you doing in my valley?"

The Monster opened his little dim eyes and blinked across the mountains.

"Who's that?" he grumbled, and it was as if distant thunder rumbled across the valley.

"Can't you see? I am bigger than you!" Coyote stirred the grass and made it wave as if it hid another monster.

"No, I can't see you. My eyes are dim. But I can eat you, Coyote! I have swallowed all the others!"

"You won't eat me! My medicine-magic is many times more powerful than yours."

"Prove it then," the Monster rumbled. "Draw in your breath and swallow me down."

Coyote drew and drew in his breath, but the Monster shivered and clung with his claws, and never moved from the valley.

"It's my turn now," growled the Monster at last. "Now, Coyote, I'll draw you."

The Monster drew and drew in his breath, and it was as if a hot wind went whistling through the trees. Branches bent and broke and crashed to the ground, and Coyote was plucked from the tree and lashed about like a whip at the end of the grapevine. Fearing that he would be dashed to pieces, he took out one of his flint knives and sawed away at the vine. It parted with a twang and off he went whizzing, toward the great red mouth of the Monster.

Over the valley, through the pass he flew, and then rows of teeth met with a snap above him and he found himself in darkness.

Luckily Coyote was able to see in the dark. He was in a long passage, in the Monster's throat, and a Rattlesnake came wriggling up beside him.

"I see he's swallowed you just like anyone else," hissed the Snake. "Fine medicine man you turned out to be."

Coyote trod on the Rattlesnake's head, and left it flat forever. Then he went on down the slippery passage until he came to the Monster's stomach. This was a huge, vaulted chamber, encased in the ribs of the Monster. On every side he saw piles of bones, and living animals among them, sighing with hunger. Fox was a shadow, and Wolf as well, and even little Black Bear had lost most of his fat.

"Now it's you, Coyote," they said to him bitterly, and they reproached him just as the Rattlesnake had for sharing their misfortunes. "Fine medicine man you are, to be sucked in too."

"Get up," Coyote told them. "Follow me."

Weary and sick and weak as they were, they did as Coyote told them, keeping close together in the dark, slippery passages. They came to another vaulted chamber, and high above them swung the Monster's heart. Here Coyote built a fire with the pitch pine. As soon as the Monster felt the heat below his heart, he started to stir in discomfort.

"Come out, Coyote!" he began to shout. "I'm sorry I ever swallowed you, Coyote! Come out, come out, Coyote! I'll let you go!"

But Coyote was climbing up the ribs of the roof, where he began to saw at the mighty cords that held the great swinging heart. The first knife broke, and the second, and the third, but Coyote continued to saw away with the fourth. Now the flame was burning hot below the Monster's heart and he writhed and snorted and bellowed in his pain.

"Coyote! Coyote! Come out! Come out!" he howled.

But Coyote only threw another stick on the fire.

Inside the Monster all was horrible confusion. The chamber rocked like a buffalo boat in the rapids. The animals were tossed from side to side, and deafened by his howls of pain. The fourth knife broke, and Coyote took up the fifth to hack at the last cord holding the giant heart. The Monster thrashed madly, the flames leaped high, the last heavy cord parted. Down fell the Monster's heart within him, and he rolled over, dead. As soon as the animals could pick themselves up, they built a ladder of the old dry bones and climbed out safely into the sunshine through the yawning mouth.

How good the air felt, how welcome was the sunlight, and the smell of the grass crushed down by the Monster's writhing! With never a word of gratitude, they shouted for joy as they leaped to the ground and set off about their business.

"You, there, come back!" Coyote shouted. "What are we going to do with the Monster's body?"

"Why do anything?" asked Fox, and the others agreed. "Just leave it there."

"Leave it there?" asked Coyote. "Don't you realize? Very soon now the human race will be coming! The valley must be cleared out and made ready for the people!"

So, using the last of his sharp flint knives, he started to carve up the Monster. He piled the meat on one side and the bones on the other, and each of the piles was like a little mountain. Then Coyote took the thigh bone and flung it far over the Sawtooth Mountains, saying, "Here shall be born the tall, long-legged people." And in that land there sprang up the Blackfoot Indians, a tall, long-legged race.

He threw the fat over the Rocky Mountains, into the Dakota Country. And later the great Sioux Indians came there, and they were round and fat.

The wide ribs were flung to Montana, and the Flathead Indians there were broad and squatty.

So the piles were scattered over the earth, and at last the valley was clear.

"Well," sniffed Black Bear, "I hope you're satisfied. You haven't left a splinter for your own home valley."

It was true. Coyote had been working so hard, flinging the Monster's bones about the mountains, that he had forgotten to save a piece for the

Idaho people. But a few drops of blood were left on his paws, and these he sprinkled on the ground, predicting, "The tribe that comes here will be small in numbers, but the bravest warriors of all."

And so it was. The Numipu came to Idaho, and they were the greatest fighters in the world. They conquered the Blackfeet; they conquered the Sioux; they conquered the Snakes and the Crows. But with all their triumphs in the art of war, they never forgot the Great Trickster, and even today, around the winter fires, they tell their children the stories of Coyote.

Retold by Fran Martin

How are the roles assigned to Finn Mac Cool and to Coyote similar?

How does this story explain the distinctive characteristics of several Indian tribes?

If you like sketching, you might draw one or two of the scenes described in this tale, perhaps the one inside the monster when Coyote is hacking away at the mighty heart cords, or the one where the animals climb up the ladder of old dry bones and out into the sunshine.

The Whale

At every stroke his brazen fins do take,
More circles in the broken sea they make
Than cannons' voices, when the air they tear.
His ribs are pillars, and his high arched roof
Of bark that blunts best steel is thunder-proof.
Swim in him swallowed dolphins, without fear,
And feel no sides, as if his vast womb were
Some inland sea, and ever as he went
He spouted rivers up, as if he meant
    To join our seas with seas above the firmament.

He hunts not fish, but as an officer,
Stays in his court, at his own net, and there
All suitors of all sorts themselves enthrall;
So on his back lies this whale wantoning,
And in his gulf-like throat sucks every thing
That passeth near. Fish chaseth fish, and all,
Flyer and follower, in this whirlpool fall;
O might not states of more equality
Consist? and is it of necessity
    That thousand guiltless smalls, to make one great, must die?

John Donne

This monster is a victorious destroyer. What images, or pictures, suggest his power and destructiveness? Donne says that his whale spouts up rivers of water as if he means to "join our seas with seas above the firmament." What would happen to the earth if he succeeded? Many fish, engaged in various chases or quests, are sucked in and "enthralled," or enslaved, by the whale. Do you think that this monster is only a whale and that these fish are only fish? Or do they symbolize, or stand for, something about life in an imperfect world? Do you think Donne is saying that guiltlessness or innocence (see the last line) is no protection against the very real evil encountered in the stormy sea of reality?

Donne's whale is based to some extent on the great sea monster or whale in the Bible. Compare the various monsters you've encountered so far in this First Story. Which are made to seem demonic, that is, devilish and destructive?

The Shepherd Boy Sings

in the Valley of Humiliation

He that is down needs fear no fall,
    He that is low, no pride;
He that is humble ever shall
    Have God to be his guide.

I am content with what I have,
    Little be it or much:
And, Lord, contentment still I crave,
    Because Thou savest such.

Fullness to such a burden is
    That go on pilgrimage:
Here little, and hereafter bliss,
    Is best from age to age.

John Bunyan

What mental or spiritual attitude does Bunyan say is appropriate for the pilgrim seeking heaven?

The first line of the last stanza could be reworded to say: "To such a pilgrim, fullness is a burden." What does "fullness" mean?

Do you think the shepherd boy has conquered the earth, as recommended in "O strong of heart..."?

Where My Books Go

All the words that I gather,
And all the words that I write,
Must spread out their wings untiring,
And never rest in their flight,
Till they come where your sad, sad heart is,
And sing to you in the night,
Beyond where the waters are moving,
Storm darkened or starry bright.

William Butler Yeats

Yeats's quest here and in all his speaking and writing, he says, is to reach to somewhere "Beyond where the waters are moving." Think back over this phase called "The Quest," and define the various goals or motives that move the characters.

In which of the selections can you find caves and hilltops; valleys and mountains; fire and water; night and morning?

THE POWER OF INNOCENCE

Soldier Jack

Well, Jack fin'ly joined the King's army and went off to the wars. He fought first in one country and then in another, and did pretty well. He served thirty years, and then they told him they reckoned he'd pulled his term and he could go on back home. So they gave him his dis-charge, and Jack hit the road.

Now, back in them days soldiers didn't get no pay, and all they gave a man when he left the army was two loaves of bread. Jack was a-walkin' on the highway with those loaves of lightbread stuck under his arm when he met up with a beggar, and the beggar he bummed Jack for somethin' to eat, so Jack gave him one of his loaves of bread. Then directly he met an old man with a long gray beard, and he asked Jack for some bread. Jack cut the other loaf in two and gave the old feller half of it and went on.

But he got to studyin' about that 'fore he'd gone very far, and then he turned back and caught up with the old man, says, "Daddy, I didn't do you right. I gave another man a whole loaf and I didn't give you but a half a one. Here's the rest of the loaf."

The old man thanked Jack, says, "Well, now, you're all right, Jack, and here's something I'm goin' to give you." He handed Jack a sack he had across his arm, says, "If ever you want to catch anything, you take this sack and hold it open with one hand and slap it with the other'n and say,

> *'Whickety whack!*
> *Into my sack!'*

and it'll get right in this sack for ye."

Then he took a little vial out of his pocket and gave that to Jack, says, "Now, this little glass will tell you whether somebody who's sick will die or get well. All you got to do is fill it up with clear spring water and look through it. If you see Death standin' at the foot of the bed, that person'll get well, but if Death is waitin' at the head of the bed, you'll know they're about to die."

Jack thanked the old man and went on with the sack over his shoulder and the glass in his pocket. He traveled on and traveled on, and along toward night the road went through a woodland and Jack heard some turkeys cluckin'. Looked up in a big oak tree and there set nine wild turkeys. So Jack opened the sack and slapped it, says,

> *"Whickety whack!*
> *Into my sack!"*

—and all nine of them turkeys flew right down and got in the sack. Jack pulled the mouth of the sack together and went on. He came to a town about dark, went to a ho-tel and asked could he swap his turkeys for a room and somethin' to eat. The ho-tel missus she weighed the turkeys and Jack got a room and supper and breakfast and a little change to boot.

Next day Jack went on, and about twelve he passed by a big fine house near the road, looked like nobody lived there. The yard was growed up in weeds and there wasn't no curtains in the windows, and Jack got to wonderin' about such a good house bein' empty. Met a boy in the road directly and the boy told Jack the house was ha'nted. Jack asked who did the place belong to and the boy told him. So Jack went down to that man's house and got to talkin' to him about it.

"Yes," the man told him, "that house has been ha'nted for thirty or forty years. There can't nobody stay there overnight. I've promised several fellers that if they'd stay all night up there I'd deed 'em the house and a thousand acres and give 'em a thousand dollars, but there ain't nobody ever broke the ha'nt yet."

"I'll try it," says Jack. "I'll stay there all night."

Well, that man took him up on it and they got some grub for Jack to eat while he stayed there, and the man took Jack on to the house and holp him build up a fire and then left him there. Jack sat down by the fire and got out his pipe and smoked awhile. Then he fixed his supper and eat it and lit up his pipe again and sat right on tendin' his fire ever' now and then and a-waitin'. Well, it got up 'way on in the night, and about midnight Jack heard a great roar and somethin' knockin' around upstairs and wheels a-rollin' and chains a-rattlin', and then three little devils came jumpin' down the stair steps. Jack sat right on. The little devils had some sacks of money with 'em and they came over to the fire and commenced banterin' Jack for a poker game. Jack didn't have no money except that change from the ho-tel, but he sat down and invested it, and got to winnin' off the little devils. They lost ever' time, and started tryin' to peep and see Jack's hole card, but he was slick and played close to the floor, and it wasn't long till he cleaned 'em out. Then they got mad and went to fussin' at Jack and threatenin' him with great swoards, and so Jack picked up that sack and held it open, says,

"Whickety whack!
Into my sack!"

and all three of them little devils scrouged right down in the sack. Jack pulled the mouth of the sack to and tied it, put it in one corner and then he laid down by the fire and went to sleep.

Next mornin' the man came back, and there was Jack cookin' his breakfast. Jack told him what happened and showed him the sack full of devils, so that man deeded Jack the house and the thousand acres and paid him a thousand dollars, and then they took the little devils down to the blacksmith shop and hired the blacksmith to sledge 'em for twenty-four hours. "I want you to lay the hammer to 'em," Jack told him. So he did that, and it was a sight how the sparks flew. There wasn't a thing but ashes in Jack's sack when that blacksmith got done. So Jack paid him and took the sack on home and put it up on the fireboard.

Well, Jack fixed up the house and hired boys to help him tend the land and he lived on there by himself and took it sort of easy. He was gettin' to be an old man, Jack was, and he didn't work too hard. He enjoyed lookin' after ever'thing and makin' little improve-ments around his place; but he had plenty of money, so he hired most of the heavy work done and lived right on there and saw to it that the boys made the crops pay pretty well.

Then one day word came down in that settle-ment that the King's girl was down sick and all the doctors were lookin' for her to die. They said she couldn't be cured, so the King had all the doctors' heads cut off. Then the King he put out word that anybody could cure his girl, he'd pay 'em several thousand dollars.

Well, Jack he didn't want the money, but he thought he'd go up there and see about that girl. So he got down his sack and stuck that little glass vial in his coat pocket and went on to the King's house. The King took him in where his girl was a-lyin' in the bed and Jack sent for some clear spring water. They brought it to him and he filled up that little vial, held it up and looked through it, and there was Death standin' at the head of the bed, grinnin'. Jack set the vial down and got his sack opened up, struck it with his hand, says,

"Whickety whack!
Into my sack!"

—and Death got down in the sack. Jack tied the sack up tight, and the King's girl got well, and they brought the money to Jack, but he wouldn't take it. Then Jack went on home, and he had one of the boys take that sack and tie it 'way up in the top of a big poplar tree standin' there in the yard.

Well, Jack kept on with his place and his house. The boys who worked for him, they'd grow up and get married and go off and he'd hire some others. He noticed his hair was grayin' up considerable and he growed him a beard directly and it com-menced gettin' sort of long, but Jack he enjoyed life and never paid much attention to the almanac. He kept a calendar so he could tell when it was Sunday and not work, but he never noticed what year it was. He stayed at home by himself most of the time, didn't get out much to go anywhere.

Then one spring mornin' Jack decided he'd take a walk over in the settle-ment, see friendly faces and have a little pleasure talkin' to people. He got down the road a piece and met up with an old lady. Jack looked at her and he never had seen anybody as old as she was. Her face was so wrinkled and leathery it was terrible to look at. Her eyes set 'way back in her head and her white hair was so thin it was almost gone. She was stooped over so her nose almost bumped her knees when she walked.

Jack stopped, says, "Howdy do, ma'm."

She started straightenin' up, with her bones a-crackin' and her head a-shakin' like palsy, and fin'ly she got her eyes up where she could look at Jack.

"Howdy do, son," she says.

"How you gettin' on, granny?" Jack asked her.

"Oh, law, son," she says, "it's awful."

"Why, what's the matter, granny?" says Jack.

"Matter?" she says. "Why, livin' as long as this, that's what it is."

"Yes," Jack says, "you do look sort of old-like. Just how old are ye, ma'm?"

"Next June," she says, "on the twelfth day of the month, I'll be two hundred and six years old."

"Well, I declare!" says Jack. "I never did hear of anybody gettin' to be that old."

"It ain't right," says the old lady, "livin' that long and not bein' able to die."

"You mean you want to die?"

"O Lord, yes," she told him.

"Well, why can't ye die, granny?"

"Why, ain't you heard?" the old lady asked him. "Some fool's got Death shut up in a sack. There ain't nobody died around here for a hundred and forty-two years, and you know that's against nature, now ain't it?"

Jack turned around right there and went on back home. He studied about what the old lady said for a day or two, then he called one of his boys to climb up in that poplar tree and bring him down the sack was up there. The boy cloomb up and brought the sack in to Jack. Jack took his knife and cut the sack where he'd tied it, and when Death got loose, all the old folks com-menced droppin' dead wherever they was. And Jack was about the first one Death got, I reckon.

Retold by Gaines Kilgore, James Adams, and Richard Chase

What qualities in Jack enable him to conquer Death? Why, though, does he decide to let Death free again after all?

The Fish and the Ring

Once upon a time, there was a mighty baron in the North Countrie who was a great magician and knew everything that would come to pass. So one day, when his little boy was four years old, he looked into the Book of Fate to see what would happen to him. And to his dismay, he found that his son would wed a lowly maid that had just been born in a house under the shadow of York Minster. Now the Baron knew the father of the little girl was very, very poor, and he had five children already. So he called for his horse, and rode into York, and passed by the father's house, and saw him sitting by the door, sad and doleful. So he dismounted and went up to him and said: "What is the matter, my good man?" And the man said: "Well, your honor, the fact is, I've five children already, and now a sixth's come, a little lass, and where to get the bread from to fill their mouths, that's more than I can say."

"Don't be downhearted, my man," said the Baron. "If that's your trouble, I can help you. I'll take away the last little one, and you won't have to bother about her."

"Thank you kindly, sir," said the man; and he went in and brought out the lass and gave her to the Baron, who mounted his horse and rode away with her. And when he got by the bank of the river Ouse, he threw the little thing into the river, and rode off to his castle.

But the little lass didn't sink; her clothes kept her up for a time, and she floated and she floated, till she was cast ashore just in front of a fisherman's hut. There the fisherman found her, and took pity on the poor little thing and took her into his house, and she lived there till she was fifteen years old, and a fine handsome girl.

One day it happened that the Baron went out hunting with some companions along the banks of the River Ouse, and stopped at the fisherman's hut to get a drink, and the girl came out to give it to them. They all noticed her beauty, and one of them said to the Baron: "You can read fates, Baron, whom will she marry, d'ye think?"

"Oh! that's easy to guess," said the Baron; "some yokel or other. But I'll cast her horoscope. Come here, girl, and tell me on what day you were born."

"I don't know, sir," said the girl, "I was picked up just here after having been brought down by the river about fifteen years ago."

Then the Baron knew who she was, and when they went away, he rode back and said to the girl: "Hark ye, girl, I will make your fortune. Take this letter to my brother in Scarborough, and you will be settled for life." And the girl took the letter and said she would go. Now this was what he had written in the letter:

"DEAR BROTHER,—Take the bearer and put her to death immediately.
"Yours affectionately,
"HUMPHREY."

So soon after the girl set out for Scarborough, and slept for the night at a little inn. Now that very night a band of robbers broke into the inn, and searched the girl, who had no money, and only the letter. So they opened this and read it, and thought it a shame. The captain of the robbers took a pen and paper and wrote this letter:

"DEAR BROTHER,—Take the bearer and marry her to my son immediately.
"Yours affectionately,
"HUMPHREY."

And then he gave it to the girl, bidding her begone. So she went on to the Baron's brother at Scarborough, a noble knight, with whom the Baron's son was staying. When she gave the letter to his brother, he gave orders for the wedding to be prepared at once, and they were married that very day.

Soon after, the Baron himself came to his brother's castle, and what was his surprise to find the very thing he had plotted against had come to pass. But he was not to be put off that way; and he took the girl out for a walk, as he said, along the cliffs. And when he got her all alone, he took her by the arms, and was going to throw her over. But she begged hard for her life. "I have not done anything," she said: "if you will only spare me, I will do whatever you wish. I will never see you or your son again till you desire it." Then the Baron took off his gold ring and threw it into the sea, saying: "Never let me see your face till you can show me that ring"; and he let her go.

The poor girl wandered on and on, till at last she came to a great noble's castle, and she asked to have some work given to her; and they made her the scullion girl of the castle, for she had been used to such work in the fisherman's hut.

Now one day, who should she see coming up to the noble's house but the Baron and his brother and his son, her husband. She didn't know what to do; but thought they would not see her in the castle kitchen. So she went back to her work with a sigh, and set to cleaning a huge big fish that was to be boiled for their dinner. And, as she was cleaning it, she saw something shine inside it, and what do you think she found? Why, there was the Baron's ring, the very one he had thrown over the cliff at Scarborough. She was glad indeed to see it, you may be sure. Then she cooked the fish as nicely as she could, and served it up.

Well, when the fish came on the table, the guests liked it so well that they asked the noble who cooked it. He said he didn't know, but called to his servants: "Ho, there, send the cook who cooked that fine fish." So they went down to the kitchen and told the girl she was wanted in the hall. Then she made herself ready and put the Baron's gold ring on her thumb and went up into the hall.

When the banqueters saw such a young and beautiful cook they were surprised. But the Baron was in a tower of a temper, and started up as if he would do her some violence. So the girl went up to him with her hand before her with the ring on it; and she put it down before him on the table. Then at last the Baron saw that no one could fight against Fate, and he handed her to a seat and announced to all the company that this was his son's true wife; and he took her and his son home to his castle; and they all lived as happy as could be ever afterwards.

Retold by Joseph Jacobs

How is this girl's infancy similar to Zal's? What finally helps her out of her troubles? How would you describe the end of the story?

Beauty and the Beast

There was once a very rich merchant, who had six children, three boys and three girls, for whose education he very wisely spared no expense. The three daughters were all handsome, but particularly the youngest, who was so very beautiful that in her childhood everyone called her Beauty. Since she was equally lovely when grown up, nobody called her by any other name, which made her sisters very jealous of her. This youngest daughter was not only more handsome than her sisters, but also was better tempered. The others were vain of their wealth and position. They gave themselves a thousand airs, and refused to visit other merchants' daughters; nor would they condescend to be seen except with persons of quality. They went every day to balls, plays, and public places, and always made game of their youngest sister, who often spent her leisure in reading or other useful work. As it was well known that these young ladies would have large fortunes many great merchants wished to get them for wives; but the two eldest always answered that, for their parts, they had no thought of marrying anyone below a duke or an earl at least. Beauty had quite as many offers as her sisters, but she always answered, with the greatest civility, that though she was much obliged to her lovers she would rather live some years longer with her father, as she thought herself too young to marry.

It happened that by some unlucky accident the merchant suddenly lost all his fortune, and had nothing left but a small cottage in the country. Upon this he said to his daughters, while the tears ran down his cheeks, "My children, we must now go and dwell in the cottage, and try to get a living by labor, for we have no other means of support."

The two eldest replied that they did not know how to work, and would not leave town, for they had lovers enough who would be glad to marry them, though they had no longer any fortune. But in this they were mistaken, for when the lovers heard what had happened they said that as the girls were so proud and ill-tempered they were not sorry at all to see their pride brought down. They could now show off to their cows and sheep. But everybody pitied poor Beauty, because she was so sweet-tempered and kind to all, and several gentlemen offered to marry her, though she had not a penny; but Beauty still refused, and said she could not think of leaving her poor father in this trouble. At first Beauty could not help sometimes crying in secret for the hardships she was now obliged to suffer; but in a very short time she said to herself, "All the crying in the world will do me no good, so I will try to be happy without a fortune."

When they had removed to their cottage the merchant and his three sons employed themselves in plowing and sowing the fields and working in the garden. Beauty also did her part, for she rose by four o'clock every morning, lighted the fires, cleaned the house, and got ready the breakfast for the whole family. At first she found all this very hard; but she soon grew quite used to it, and thought it no hardship. Indeed, the work greatly benefited her health, and made her more beautiful still, and when she had done all that was necessary she used to amuse herself with reading, playing her music, or singing while she spun. But her two sisters were at a loss what to do to pass the time away. They had their breakfast in bed, and did not rise till ten o'clock. Then they commonly walked out, but always found themselves very soon tired, when they would often sit down under a shady tree and grieve for the loss of their carriage and fine clothes, and say to each other, "What a mean-spirited, poor, stupid creature our young sister is to be so content with this low way of life!" But their father thought differently, and loved and admired his youngest child more than ever.

After they had lived in this manner about a year the merchant received a letter which informed him that one of his richest ships, which he thought was lost, had just come into port. This news made the two eldest sisters almost mad with joy, for they thought they would now leave the cottage and have all their finery again. When they found that their father must take a journey to the ship the two eldest begged he would not fail to bring them back some new gowns, caps, rings, and all sorts of trinkets. But Beauty asked for nothing; for she thought in herself that all the ship was worth would hardly buy everything her sisters wished for. "Beauty," said the merchant, "how comes it that you asked for nothing? What can I bring you, my child?"

"Since you are so kind as to think of me, dear Father," she answered, "I should be glad if you would bring me a rose, for we have none in our garden."

Now Beauty did not indeed wish for a rose, nor anything else, but she only said this that she might not affront her sisters; otherwise they would have said she wanted her father to praise her for desiring nothing.

The merchant took his leave of them, and set out on his journey; but when he got to the ship some persons went to law with him about the cargo, and after a deal of trouble and several months' delay he started back to his cottage as poor as he had left it. When he was within thirty miles of his home, in spite of the joy he felt at again meeting his children, he could not help thinking of the presents he had promised to bring them, particularly of the rose for Beauty, which, as it was now midwinter, he could by no means have found for her. It rained hard, and then it began to snow, and before long he had lost his way.

Night came on, and he feared he would die of cold and hunger, or be torn to pieces by the wolves that he heard howling round him. All at once he cast his eyes toward a long avenue, and saw at the end a light, but it seemed a great way off. He made the best of his way toward it, and found that it came from a splendid palace, the windows of which were all blazing with light. It had great bronze gates, standing wide open, and fine courtyards, through which the merchant passed; but not a living soul was to be seen. There were stables too, which his poor, starved horse entered at once, making a good meal of oats and hay. His master then tied him up and walked toward the entrance-hall, but still without seeing a single creature. He went on to a large dining-parlor, where he found a good fire and a table covered with some very appetizing dishes, but only one plate with a knife and fork. As the snow and rain had wetted him to the skin he went up to the fire to dry himself. "I hope," said he, "the master of the house or his servants will excuse me, for it surely will not be long now before I see them." He waited some time, but still nobody came; at last the clock struck eleven, and the merchant, being quite faint for the want of food, helped himself to a chicken and to a few glasses of wine, yet all the time trembling with fear. He sat till the clock struck twelve, and then, taking courage, began to think he might as well look about him, so he opened a door at the end of the hall, and went through it into a very grand room, in which there was a fine bed; and as he was feeling very weary he shut the door, took off his clothes, and got into it.

It was ten o'clock in the morning before he awoke, when he was amazed to see a handsome new suit of clothes laid ready for him, instead of his own, which were all torn and spoiled. "To be sure," he said to himself, "this place belongs to some good fairy who has taken pity on my ill luck." He looked out of the window, and though far away there were the snow-covered hills and the wintry wood where he had lost himself the night before, within the palace grounds he saw the most charming arbors covered with all kinds of summer flowers blooming in the sunshine. Returning to the hall where he supped, he found a breakfast-table, ready prepared. "Indeed, my good fairy," said the merchant aloud, "I am vastly obliged to you for your kind care of me." He then made a hearty breakfast, took his hat, and was going to the stable to pay his horse a visit; but as he passed under one of the arbors, which was loaded with roses, he thought of what Beauty had asked him to bring back to her, and so he took a bunch of roses to carry home. At the same moment he heard a loud noise, and saw coming toward him a beast, so frightful to look at that he was ready to faint with fear.

"Ungrateful man!" said the Beast in a terrible voice. "I have saved your life by admitting you into my palace, and in return you steal my roses, which I value more than anything I possess. But you shall atone for your fault: you shall die in a quarter of an hour."

The merchant fell on his knees, and, clasping his hands, said, "Sir, I humbly beg your pardon. I did not think it would offend you to gather a rose for one of my daughters, who had entreated me to bring her one home. Do not kill me, my lord!"

"I am not a lord, but a beast," replied the monster. "I hate false compliments, so do not fancy that you can coax me by any such ways. You tell me that you have daughters; now I will suffer you to escape if one of them will come and die in your stead. If not, promise that you will yourself return in three months, to be dealt with as I may choose."

The tender-hearted merchant had no thoughts of letting any one of his daughters die for his sake; but he knew that if he seemed to accept the beast's terms he should at least have the pleasure of seeing them once again. So he gave his promise, and was told he might then set off as soon as he liked. "But," said the Beast, "I do not wish you to go back empty-handed. Go to the room you slept in, and you will find a chest there; fill it with whatsoever you like best, and I will have it taken to your own house for you."

When the Beast had said this he went away. The good merchant, left to himself, began to consider that as he must die—for he had no thought of breaking a promise, made even to a Beast—he might as well have the comfort of leaving his children provided for. He returned to the room he had slept in, and found there heaps of gold pieces lying about. He filled the chest with them to the very brim, locked it, and, mounting his horse, left the palace and the garden full of flowers as sorrowful as he had been glad when he first beheld it.

The horse took a path across the snowy forest of his own accord, and in a few hours they reached the merchant's house. His children came running to meet him, but, instead of kissing them with joy, he could not help weeping as he looked at them. He held in his hand the bunch of roses, which he gave to Beauty, saying, "Take these roses, Beauty; but little do you think how dear they have cost your poor father." Then he gave them an account of all that he had seen or heard in the palace of the Beast.

The two eldest sisters now began to shed tears, and to lay the blame upon Beauty, who, they said, would be the cause of her father's death. "See," said they, "what happens from the pride of the little wretch. Why did not she ask for such things as we did? But, of course, she could not be like other people, and though she will be the cause of her father's death, yet she does not shed a tear."

"It would be useless," replied Beauty, "for my father shall not die. As the Beast will accept one of his daughters, I will give myself up, and be only too happy to prove my love for the best of fathers."

"No, sister," said the three brothers with one voice, "that cannot be; we will go in search of this monster, and either he or ourselves shall perish."

"Do not hope to kill him," said the merchant: "his power is far too great. But Beauty's young life shall not be sacrificed. I am old, and cannot expect to live much longer, so I shall but give up a few years of my life, and shall only grieve for the sake of my children."

"Never, Father!" cried Beauty. "If you go back to the palace you cannot hinder my going after you. Though young, I am not overfond of life; and I would much rather be eaten up by the monster than die of grief for your loss."

The merchant in vain tried to reason with Beauty, who still obstinately kept to her purpose, which, in truth, made her two sisters glad, for they were jealous of her because everybody loved her.

The merchant was so grieved at the thought of losing his child that he never once thought of the chest filled with gold; but at night, to his great surprise, he found it standing by his bedside. He said nothing about his riches to his eldest daughters, for he knew very well it would at once make them want to return to town; but he told Beauty his secret, and she then said that while he was away two gentlemen had been on a visit at their cottage, who had fallen in love with her two sisters. She entreated her father to marry them without delay, for she was so sweet-natured she only wished them to be happy.

Three months went by, only too fast, and then the merchant and Beauty got ready to set out for the palace of the Beast. Upon this the two sisters rubbed their eyes with an onion, to make believe they were crying, but both the merchant and his sons cried in earnest. Only Beauty shed no tears. They reached the palace in a very few hours, and the horse, without bidding, went into the same stable as before. The merchant and Beauty walked toward the large hall, where they found a table covered with every dainty, and two plates laid ready. The merchant had very little appetite; but Beauty, that she might the better hide her grief, placed herself at the table, and helped her father. She then began to eat herself, and thought all the time that to be sure the Beast had a mind to fatten her before he ate her up, since he had provided such good cheer for her. When they had done their supper they heard a great noise, and the good old man began to bid his poor child farewell, for he knew it was the Beast coming to them. When Beauty first saw that frightful form she was very much terrified, but tried to hide her fear. The creature walked up to her, and eyed her all over, then asked her in a dreadful voice if she had come quite of her own accord.

"Yes," said Beauty.

"Then you are a good girl, and I am very much obliged to you."

This was such an astonishingly civil answer that Beauty's courage rose; but it sank again when the Beast, addressing the merchant, desired him to leave the palace next morning and never return to it again. "And so good night, merchant. And good night, Beauty."

"Good night, Beast," she answered, as the monster shuffled out of the room.

"Ah, my dear child," said the merchant, kissing his daughter, "I am half dead already at the thought of leaving you with this dreadful Beast; you shall go back and let me stay in your place."

"No," said Beauty boldly, "I will never agree to that; you must go home tomorrow morning."

They then wished each other good night, and went to bed, both of them thinking they should not be able to close their eyes; but they immediately fell into a deep sleep, and did not wake till morning. Beauty dreamed that a lady came up to her, who said, "I am very pleased, Beauty, that you have been willing to give your life to save that of your father. Do not be afraid; you shall not go without a reward."

As soon as Beauty awoke, she told her father this dream: but though it gave him some comfort he was a long time before he could be persuaded to leave the palace. At last Beauty succeeded in getting him safely away.

When her father was out of sight poor Beauty began to weep sorely; still, having naturally a courageous spirit, she soon resolved not to make her sad case still worse by useless sorrow, but to wait and be patient. She walked through the rooms of the palace, and the elegance of every part of it much charmed her.

But what was her surprise when she came to a door on which was written "BEAUTY'S ROOM"! When she opened it her eyes were dazzled by the splendor and taste of the apartment. What made her wonder more than all the rest was a large library filled with books, a harpsichord, and many pieces of music. "The Beast surely does not mean to eat me up immediately," said she, "since he takes care I shall not be at a loss how to amuse myself." She opened the library, and saw these verses written in letters of gold on the back of one of the books:

> *Beauteous lady, dry your tears;*
> *Here's no cause for sighs or fears.*
> *Command as freely as you may,*
> *For you command, and I obey.*

"Alas," said she, sighing, "I wish I could only command a sight of my poor father, and know what he is doing at this moment." Just then, by chance, she cast her eyes on a looking-glass that stood near her, and in it she saw a picture of her old home, and her father riding mournfully up to the door. Her sisters came out to meet him, and although they tried to look sorry it was easy to see that in their hearts they were very glad. In a short time all this picture disappeared, but it caused Beauty to think that the Beast, besides being very powerful, was also very kind. About the middle of the day she found a table laid ready for her, and sweet music was played all the time she was dining, although she could not see anybody. But at supper, when she was going to seat herself at table, she heard the noise of the Beast, and could not help trembling with fear.

"Beauty," said he, "will you give me leave to see you sup?"

"That is as you please," answered she, very much afraid.

"Not in the least," said the Beast. "You alone command in this place. If you should not like my company you need only say so, and I will leave you this moment. But tell me, Beauty, do you not think me very ugly?"

"Why yes," said she, "for I cannot tell a falsehood; but then I think you are very good."

"Am I?" sadly replied the Beast. "Yet besides being ugly, I am also very stupid; I know well enough that I am but a beast."

"Very stupid people," said Beauty, "are never aware of it themselves."

At this kindly speech the Beast looked pleased, and replied, not without an awkward sort of politeness, "Pray do not let me detain you from supper, and be sure that you are well served. All you see is your own, and I should be deeply grieved if you wanted for anything."

"You are very kind—so kind that I almost forgot you are so ugly," said Beauty earnestly.

"Ah, yes!" answered the Beast with a great sigh. "I hope I am good-tempered, but still I am only a monster."

"There is many a monster who wears the form of a man. It is better of the two to have the heart of a man and the form of a monster."

"I would thank you, Beauty, for this speech, but I am too stupid to say anything that would please you," returned the Beast in a melancholy voice; and altogether he seemed so gentle and so unhappy that Beauty, who had the tenderest heart in the world, felt her fear of him gradually vanish.

She ate her supper with a good appetite, and talked in her own sensible and charming way, till at last, when the Beast rose to depart, he terrified her more than ever by saying abruptly, in his gruff voice, "Beauty, will you marry me?"

Now Beauty, frightened as she was, would speak only the exact truth: her father had told her that the Beast liked only to have the truth spoken to him. So she answered in a very firm tone, "No, Beast."

He did not go into a passion, or do anything but sigh deeply and depart.

When Beauty found herself alone she began to feel pity for the poor Beast. "Oh," said she, "what a sad thing it is that he should be so very frightful, since he is so good-tempered!"

Beauty lived three months in this palace very well pleased. The Beast came to see her every night, and talked with her while she supped; and though what he said was not very clever, yet she saw in him every day some new goodness. So, instead of dreading the time of his coming, she soon began continually looking at her watch, to see if it were nine o'clock, for that was the hour when he never failed to visit her. One thing only vexed her, which was that every night before he went away he always made it a rule to ask her if she would be his wife, and seemed very much grieved when she firmly answered, "No." At last, one night, she said to him, "You wound me greatly, Beast, by forcing me to refuse you so often; I wish I could take such a liking to you as to agree to marry you; but I must tell you plainly that I do not think it will ever happen. I shall always be your friend; so try to let that content you."

"I must," sighed the Beast, "for I know well enough how frightful I am; but I love you better than myself. Yet I think I am very lucky in your being pleased to stay with me. Now promise me, Beauty, that you will never leave me."

Beauty would almost have agreed to this, so sorry was she for him, but she had that day seen in her magic glass, which she looked at constantly, that her father was dying of grief for her sake.

"Alas," she said, "I long so much to see my father that if you do not give me leave to visit him I shall break my heart."

"I would rather break mine, Beauty," answered the Beast. "I will send you to your father's cottage: you shall stay there, and your poor Beast shall die of sorrow."

"No," said Beauty, crying, "I love you too well to be the cause of your death; I promise to return in a week. You have shown me that my

sisters are married and my brothers are gone for soldiers, so that my father is left all alone. Let me stay a week with him."

"You shall find yourself with him tomorrow morning," replied the Beast; "but, mind, do not forget your promise. When you wish to return you have nothing to do but to put your ring on a table when you go to bed. Good-bye, Beauty!" The Beast sighed as he said these words, and Beauty went to bed very sorry to see him so much grieved. When she awoke in the morning she found herself in her father's cottage. She rang a bell that was at her bedside, and a servant entered; but as soon as she saw Beauty, the woman gave a loud shriek, upon which the merchant ran upstairs, and when he beheld his daughter he ran to her and kissed her a hundred times. At last Beauty began to remember that she had brought no clothes with her to put on; but the servant told her she had just found in the next room a large chest full of dresses, trimmed all over with gold, and adorned with precious stones.

Beauty, in her own mind, thanked the Beast for his kindness, and put on the plainest gown she could find among them all. She then desired the servant to lay the rest aside, for she intended to give them to her sisters; but as soon as she had spoken these words the chest was gone out of sight in a moment. Her father then suggested that perhaps the Beast chose for her to keep them all for herself; and as soon as he had said this they saw the chest standing again in the same place. While Beauty was dressing herself a servant brought word to her that her sisters were come with their husbands to pay her a visit. They both lived unhappily with the gentlemen they had married. The husband of the eldest was very handsome, but was so proud of this that he thought of nothing else from morning till night, and did not care a pin for the beauty of his wife. The second had married a man of great learning; but he made no use of it, except to torment and affront all his friends, and his wife more than any of them. The two sisters were ready to burst with spite when they saw Beauty dressed like a princess, and looking so very charming. All the kindness that she showed them was of no use, for they were vexed more than ever when she told them how happy she lived at the palace of the Beast. The spiteful creatures went by themselves into the garden, where they cried to think of her good fortune.

"Why should the little wretch be better off than we?" said they. "We are much handsomer than she is."

"Sister," said the eldest, "a thought has just come into my head: let us try to keep her here longer than the week for which the Beast gave her leave; and then he will be so angry that perhaps when she goes back to him he will eat her up in a moment."

"That is a good idea," answered the other; "but to do this we must pretend to be very kind."

They then went to join her in the cottage, where they showed her so much false love that Beauty could not help crying for joy.

When the week was ended the two sisters began to pretend such grief at the thought of her leaving them that she agreed to stay a week more; but all that time Beauty could not help fretting for the sorrow that she knew her absence would give her poor Beast, for she tenderly loved him, and much wished for his company again. Among all the grand and clever people she saw she found nobody who was half so sensible, so affectionate, so thoughtful, or so kind. The tenth night of her being at the cottage she dreamed she was in the garden of the palace, that the Beast lay dying on a grass-plot, and with his last breath put her in mind of her promise, and laid his death to her forsaking him. Beauty awoke in a great fright, and burst into tears. "Am not I wicked," said she, "to behave so ill to a Beast who has shown me so much kindness? Why do I not marry him? I am sure I should be more happy with him than my sisters are with their husbands. He shall not be wretched any longer on my account, for I should do nothing but blame myself all the rest of my life."

She then rose, put her ring on the table, got into bed again, and soon fell asleep. In the morning she with joy found herself in the palace of the Beast. She dressed herself very carefully, that she might please him the better, and thought she had never known a day pass away so slowly. At last the clock struck nine, but the Beast did not come. Beauty, dreading lest she might truly have caused his death, ran from room to room, calling out, "Beast, dear Beast"; but there was no answer. At last she remembered her dream, rushed to the grass-plot, and there saw him lying apparently dead beside the fountain. Forgetting all his ugliness, she threw herself upon him, and, finding his heart still beating, she fetched some water and sprinkled it over him, weeping and sobbing the while.

The Beast opened his eyes. "You forgot your promise, Beauty, and so I determined to die, for I could not live without you. I have starved myself to death, but I shall die content, since I have seen your face once more."

"No, dear Beast," cried Beauty passionately, "you shall not die; you shall live to be my husband. I thought it was only friendship I felt for you, but now I know it was love."

The moment Beauty had spoken these words the palace was suddenly lighted up, and all kinds of rejoicings were heard around them, none of which she noticed, but continued to hang over her dear Beast with the utmost tenderness. At last, unable to restrain herself, she dropped her head over her hands, covered her eyes, and cried for joy; and when she looked up again the Beast was gone. In his stead she saw at her feet a handsome, graceful young prince, who thanked her with the tenderest expressions for having freed him from enchantment.

"But where is my poor Beast? I only want him, and nobody else," sobbed Beauty.

"I am he," replied the prince. "A wicked fairy condemned me to this form, and forbade me to show that I had any wit or sense till a beautiful lady should consent to marry me. You alone, dearest Beauty, judged me neither by my looks nor by my talents, but by my heart alone. Take it, then, and all that I have besides, for all is yours."

Beauty, full of surprise, but very happy, suffered the prince to lead her to his palace, where she found her father and sisters, who had been brought there by the fairy-lady whom she had seen in a dream the first night she came.

"Beauty," said the fairy, "you have chosen well, and you have your reward, for a true heart is better than either good looks or clever brains. As for you, ladies"—and she turned to the two elder sisters—"I know all your ill deeds, but I have no worse punishment for you than to see your sister happy. You shall stand as statues at the door of her palace, and when you repent of and have amended your faults you shall become women again. But, to tell you the truth, I very much fear you will remain statues for ever."

Madame de Villeneuve

Mr. Fox

Lady Mary was young, and Lady Mary was fair. She had two brothers, and more lovers than she could count. But of them all, the bravest and most gallant was a Mr. Fox, whom she met when she was down at her father's country house. No one knew who Mr. Fox was; but he was certainly brave, and surely rich, and of all her lovers, Lady Mary cared for him alone. At last it was agreed upon between them that they should be married. Lady Mary asked Mr. Fox where they should live, and he described to her his castle, and where it was; but, strange to say, did not ask her or her brothers to come and see it.

So one day, near the wedding day, when her brothers were out, and Mr. Fox was away for a day or two on business, as he said, Lady Mary set out for Mr. Fox's castle. And after many searchings, she came at last to it, and a fine strong house it was, with high walls and a deep moat. And when she came up to the gateway she saw written on it:

Be bold, be bold.

But as the gate was open, she went through it, and found no one there. So she went up to the doorway, and over it she found written:

Be bold, be bold, but not too bold.

Still she went on, till she came into the hall, and went up the broad stairs till she came to a door in the gallery, over which was written:

Be bold, be bold, but not too bold,
Lest that your heart's blood should run cold.

But Lady Mary was a brave one, she was, and she opened the door, and what do you think she saw? Why, bodies and skeletons of beautiful young ladies all stained with blood. So Lady Mary thought it was high time to get out of that horrid place, and she closed the door, went through the gallery, and was just going down the stairs, and out of the hall, when who should she see through the window, but Mr. Fox dragging a beautiful young lady along from the gateway to the door. Lady Mary rushed downstairs, and hid herself behind a cask, just in time, as Mr. Fox came in with the poor young lady who seemed to have fainted. Just as he got near Lady Mary, Mr. Fox saw a diamond ring glittering on the finger of the young lady he was dragging, and he tried to pull it off. But it was tightly fixed, and would not come off, so Mr. Fox cursed and swore, and drew his sword, raised it, and brought it down upon the hand of the poor lady. The sword cut off the hand, which jumped up into the air, and fell of all places in the world into Lady Mary's lap. Mr. Fox looked about a bit, but did not think of looking behind the cask, so at last he went on dragging the young lady up the stairs into the Bloody Chamber.

As soon as she heard him pass through the gallery, Lady Mary crept out of the door, down through the gateway, and ran home as fast as she could.

Now it happened that the very next day the marriage contract of Lady Mary and Mr. Fox was to be signed, and there was a splendid breakfast before that. And when Mr. Fox was seated at table opposite Lady Mary, he looked at her. "How pale you are this morning, my dear." "Yes," said she, "I had a bad night's rest last night. I had horrible dreams." "Dreams go by contraries," said Mr. Fox; "but tell us your dream, and your sweet voice will make the time pass till the happy hour comes."

"I dreamed," said Lady Mary, "that I went yestermorn to your castle, and I found it in the woods, with high walls, and a deep moat, and over the gateway was written:

Be bold, be bold.

"But it is not so, nor it was not so," said Mr. Fox.

"And when I came to the doorway, over it was written:

Be bold, be bold, but not too bold.

"It is not so, nor it was not so," said Mr. Fox.

"And then I went upstairs, and came to a gallery, at the end of which was a door, on which was written:

Be bold, be bold, but not too bold,
Lest that your heart's blood should run cold.

"It is not so, nor it was not so," said Mr. Fox.

"And then—and then I opened the door, and the room was filled with bodies and skeletons of poor dead women, all stained with their blood."

"It is not so, nor it was not so. And God forbid it should be so," said Mr. Fox.

"I then dreamed that I rushed down the gallery, and just as I was going down the stairs, I saw you, Mr. Fox, coming up to the hall door, dragging after you a poor young lady, rich and beautiful."

"It is not so, nor it was not so. And God forbid it should be so," said Mr. Fox.

"I rushed downstairs, just in time to hide myself behind a cask, when you, Mr. Fox, came in dragging the young lady by the arm. And, as you passed me, Mr. Fox, I thought I saw you try and get off her diamond ring, and when you could not, Mr. Fox, it seemed to me in my dream, that you out with your sword and hacked off the poor lady's hand to get the ring."

"It is not so, nor it was not so. And God forbid it should be so," said Mr. Fox, and was going to say something else as he rose from his seat, when Lady Mary cried out:

"But it is so, and it was so. Here's hand and ring I have to show," and pulled out the lady's hand from her dress, and pointed it straight at Mr. Fox.

At once her brothers and her friends drew their swords and cut Mr. Fox into a thousand pieces.

Retold by Joseph Jacobs

"A true heart is better than either good looks or clever brains." Discuss this statement in terms of the three preceding folk tales. Consider the way the human figures in these tales are handled. Are they convincingly realistic in the light of what you know of actual human behavior? What of the "human monsters" that must be defeated?

Can it be said, in the case of each story, that the "monsters" were "tamed" or controlled by innocent maidens?

The Lady of the Lake

Sir Walter Scott

Characters

"JAMES FITZ-JAMES," *"Knight of Snowdoun," really the King of Scotland in disguise*

JAMES BOTHWELL, *Earl of Douglas—once tutor to King James V, now exiled, with all his clan, on account of the ambition of his kinsman, who, acting as regent during the minority of the King, strove to retain his power when the time had come for him to give it up*

ELLEN, *"The Lady of the Lake," his daughter*

ALLAN-BANE, *minstrel to the House of Douglas*

MALCOLM GRAEME, *Ellen's lover*

RODERICK DHU *(Roderick the Black), of Clan Alpine, a lawless and powerful Highland chieftain, who loves Ellen Douglas*

MALISE, *Roderick's henchman*

BRIAN THE HERMIT

HUGH OF LARBERT *and* JOHN OF ALLOA, *two strong men*

LEWIS OF TULLIBARDINE, *captain of the king's guard*

CLANSMEN OF RODERICK, SOLDIERS OF THE ROYAL GUARD, CITIZENS OF STIRLING, MORRIS-DANCERS, A HERALD

Appearance and Dress of the Chief Characters

RODERICK, DOUGLAS, GRAEME, and the CLANSMEN OF RODERICK wear kilts and plaids. Their shoes are bound on their feet with thongs of hide: they carry targes or shields made of hide, spears, and swords. DOUGLAS is gray-haired, but straight as a young man. His appearance suggests great muscular strength. RODERICK is dark and proud-looking. In his helmet is the plume of an eagle. MALCOLM GRAEME is slight and fair, but strongly knit. ELLEN is dark and flashing: she wears a satin snood and silken plaid. JAMES is in hunter's dress of Lincoln green, until the last act, when he wears a royal robe and a crown. ALLAN-BANE, a worn, gray-haired old man, wears the flowing robe of a minstrel, and carries a harp. BRIAN THE HERMIT is of wild appearance, with matted hair and grizzled beard. He wears a monk's frock and hood; his feet are bare. The SOLDIERS of the king's guard wear tunics of some bright color, with steel caps and breast plates, and carry spears. The MORRIS-DANCERS and revellers of Stirling are arrayed in bright fantastic clothing: the DANCERS wear bells on their hands and feet.

ACT I

Scene: The Hall of the Douglas, on an island of Loch Katrine.

On the walls hang skins, antlers, a great sword, spears, bows, etc. To the left, a bed made of heather, half-covered with a deer hide. To the right, the banner of the Douglases, blazoned with a bleeding heart. In the center of the stage, a fireplace made of stones heaped in a circle. ALLAN-BANE *sits at the right of this, striking his harp, and gazing into the embers of the dying fire. Opposite him sits* ELLEN, *weaving a garland of harebells and heather.*

ELLEN. You dream, Allan-Bane! Why do you look in the fire so intently? What do you see?

ALLAN-BANE (*in a grave monotone, almost as if he were speaking in a trance*). I see a dappled gray steed lie dead beneath the birches—a gallant steed, worthy to be ridden by a king. I see two grim staghounds of black St. Hubert's breed—hounds such as these which hunt with a king. I see a hunter in Lincoln green, a tasselled horn in his hand, a heron's plume in his cap. His eyes are the eyes of a king. Make ready, noble maid, to welcome a guest of high degree.

ELLEN (*lightly*). The ruined Douglases do not entertain noble guests. (*Rises and, going to the old man, puts her hands on his shoulders*) Arouse from your moody dream! Sing of the glory of Malcolm Graeme.

ALLAN (*solemnly*). I may strike chords of joy or glory, the strings of my harp will sound only notes of woe. So they sounded when your sainted mother died; so they sounded through Bothwell's bannered hall when the Douglases were exiled by the King.

ELLEN (*softly and proudly*).   The King loved the Douglas, my father.

ALLAN.   The King's friends did not love the pride of the Douglas clan. (*Sadly and resolutely*) If worse mishap is to come to my master or woe to my master's daughter, no future bard shall strike triumph or rapture from the strings of this harp. It shall be shivered into fragments, and shall die with me.

ELLEN (*gaily*).   Soften your fears, Allan. My father is resigned to his ill fortune. (*Twists the garland round her head and kneels before him*) So am I. These harebells are as happy as roses in a king's garden, and I am as happy as a maiden in a king's palace. When I put them in my hair, Allan, a bard is bound to swear he never saw so lovely a coronet.

ALLAN (*looking at her with admiration and regret*).   You are the loveliest and best of maidens, and you little know the honor you have lost. Might I love to see you in your rightful place, the court of Scotland, lightest in the dance, praised by all the gallants, the star of all eyes, sung by royal minstrels!

ELLEN.   I should not dance a court dance as gaily as a strathspey. I would rather listen to your song than that of a royal minstrel— and (*striking an attitude*)—as for proud suitors to bend before my conquering eye, you know, you flattering bard, that grim Sir Roderick Dhu, the terror of Loch Lomond's side, would put off a foray if I asked him—for a day, at least.

ALLAN.   Ah, the hope of the Douglas house died with him. Allied with him, the Douglas might again be great. You can guide this terrible chieftain with a silken thread.

ELLEN (*proudly*).   Allan, we owe Sir Roderick much. I would pay him with my blood, my life, but not my hand. Rather than marry him, I would wander in foreign lands, and never hear a Scottish word spoken.

(ALLAN-BANE *shakes his head and gazes dreamily into the fire. The sound of a hunting horn rings out clearly.*)

ALLAN (*again speaking as if in a trance*).   I see a hunter—carrying a tasselled horn, gaily gilt—his eyes are the eyes of a king.

ELLEN.   You dreamer! 'Tis my father's signal! Father!

(*Runs to fling open the door, and stands as if half-afraid, as she sees a hunter, with a heron's plume in his cap, a tasselled horn slung over his shoulder)*

FITZ-JAMES (*courteously*).   I am a stranger. I have lost my way, my friends, my horse, my hounds, while hunting a noble stag.

ALLAN (*looking at him fixedly*).   Your name?

FITZ-JAMES (*without hesitation*).   James Fitz-James, Knight of Snow-doun.

ELLEN (*glancing at* ALLAN-BANE).   You do not come unexpected to our lonely home. . . . We have—awaited you.

FITZ-JAMES.   Now, by the rood, my lovely maid, I have no right to claim the welcome of an expected guest. I have never breathed your mountain air before tonight, when, on this romantic island, I find a fay in fairyland.

ELLEN (*laughing and making a deep curtsey*).   Call on heaven and your lady to protect you, and enter the enchanted hall.

FITZ-JAMES (*bowing*).   My only protection must be from you, my gentle guide. (*He comes right in to the hall. Immediately the great sword on the wall falls from its place with a loud clanging sound. He starts, as if expecting treachery, looks round, and, reassured, raises the weapon with much difficulty.*) I have known but one man whose arm could raise a blade like this in the battlefield—but one man.

ELLEN (*sighs and smiles*).   That is my guardian champion's sword. It trembles as lightly in his hand as a hazel switch in mine.

FITZ-JAMES.   Your father?

ELLEN.   My father—but the giant is absent, and only a woman and an aged servant occupy his hold. Allan, put food and wine before our guest.

FITZ-JAMES.   Your father's name? Your rank and state?

ELLEN (*gaily turning the question*).   Ah! I am a weird woman, dwelling far away from tower and town. I can stem the flood; I can ride on the wind; and I can cast a spell on a wandering knight while he eats his supper.

(*Sings or speaks to music, while* ALLAN *touches his harp, and* FITZ-JAMES *eats and drinks*)

> Soldier, rest! thy warfare o'er,
>   Sleep the sleep that knows no breaking;

Dream of battled fields no more,
　　Days of danger, nights of waking.
In our isle's enchanted hall,
　　Hands unseen thy couch are strewing,
Fairy strains of music fall,
　　Every sense in slumber dewing.
Soldier, rest! thy warfare o'er,
Dream of fighting fields no more:
Sleep the sleep that knows no breaking,
Morn of toil, nor night of waking.

No rude sound shall reach thine ear,
　　Armor's clang, or war steed champing,
Trump nor pibroch [1] summon here
　　Mustering clan, or squadron tramping.
Yet the lark's shrill fife may come
　　At the daybreak from the fallow,
And the bittern sound his drum,
　　Booming from the sedgy shallow.
Ruder sounds shall none be near,
Guards nor warders challenge here,
Here's no war steed's neigh and champing,
Shouting clans, or squadrons stamping.

Now sleep well on your bed of heather. (*Spreads a skin over the couch*) Come, Allan.

(ALLAN-BANE *looks once more fixedly at the knight. Exeunt* ELLEN *and* ALLAN-BANE. JAMES *lies down as if to sleep. Then he half rises as if he were troubled, and gazes at the huge sword.*)

FITZ-JAMES. Why is it that at every turn I must think of the banished Douglases? They did me wrong. I did well to exile them. Why should they haunt me thus. (*Taunting himself*) Cannot I see a mountain maiden, but her eyes must be those of a Douglas? Cannot I see a sword, but it must match the great brand of Douglas? Tut— my senses are fevered, I must rest. (*Tells his beads*) A man can

[1] **pibroch:** a form of bagpipe music, generally a call to war.

sleep in the house of his enemy. I'll turn to rest, and dream no more. (*Sleeps*)

ACT II

Scene: The borders of Loch Katrine.

(*Enter* ELLEN, FITZ-JAMES, *and* ALLAN-BANE)

FITZ-JAMES.   Sweet Ellen, I thank you for your hospitality, and for bringing me across the lake.

ELLEN.   Follow yonder path, and you will come upon the way to Stirling.

FITZ-JAMES.   I thank you. Again, farewell.

(*Bows, kissing* ELLEN's *hand, and exit*)

ELLEN (*looking after him, and then turning to* ALLAN-BANE).   What think you of this stranger guest?

ALLAN.   What think I of him? Woe the while that brought this wanderer to our dwelling. Did you not see your father's battle brand, untouched, fall from its scabbard as the stranger set foot within the hall of the Douglas?

ELLEN.   What then?

ALLAN.   That brand was forged for Douglas the Tineman [1] by fairy lore. When he was leagued with the Hotspur that sword fell—to show the footsteps of a traitor. This place is the last sure hold of Douglas and Clan Alpine—what if this stranger is a courtly spy?

ELLEN.   He is not a spy, I stake my life on it.

(*The pibroch sounds in the distance.*)

The pibroch of Clan Alpine!

(*Enter* RODERICK DHU's CLANSMEN, *from the water. The first are fully armed, with spears and shields made of hide. They carry a banner blazoned with a pine. They are followed by the boatmen, who carry oars, which they lay down. Then come the* DOUGLAS *and* MALCOLM GRAEME. *The* DOUGLAS *goes to* ELLEN *and takes her in his arms. Last of all comes* RODERICK. *As they enter, his men sing in his praises.*)

---

[1] **Douglas the Tineman:** an ancestor of Douglas, so nicknamed because he "tined" or lost his followers in every battle he fought.

Boat Song

Marchlike

Hail to the Chief who in tri - umph ad -

van - ces! Hon - ored and blessed be the

ev - er - green Pine!_____ Long may the

tree, in his ban - ner that glan - ces,

Flour - ish the _____ shel - ter and grace of our

line! Heaven send it hap - py dew, Earth lend it

sap a - new, Gay - ly to bour - geon, and

broad - ly to grow, While ev - ery High - land glen

Sends our shout back a - gain, Ro - de - righ,

Ro - de - righ, Ro - de - righ Vich Al - pine dhu,

ho! ie - roe!_____

ho! ie - roe!_____

2 / Ours is no sapling, chance-sown by the fountain,
　　Blooming at Beltane, in winter to fade;
　When the whirlwind has stripped every leaf on the mountain,
　　The more shall Clan Alpine exult in her shade.
　　　　Moored in the rifted rock,
　　　　Proof to the tempest's shock,
　　　Firmer he roots him the ruder it blow;
　　　　Monteith and Breadalbane, then,
　　　　Echo his praise again,
　　"Roderigh Vich Alpine dhu, ho! ieroe!"

The Power of Innocence　**99**

3 / Proudly our pibroch has thrilled in Glen Fruin,
　　　And Bannochar's groans to our slogan replied;
　Glen Luss and Ross-dhu, they are smoking in ruin,
　　　And the best of Loch Lomond lie dead on her side.
　　　　Widow and Saxon maid
　　　　Long shall lament our raid,
　　　Think of Clan Alpine with fear and with woe;
　　　　Lennox and Leven-glen
　　　　Shake when they hear again,
　"Roderigh Vich Alpine dhu, ho! ieroe!"

4 / Row, vassals, row, for the pride of the Highlands!
　　　Stretch to your oars, for the evergreen Pine!
　O! that the rosebud that graces yon islands
　　　Were wreathed in a garland around him to twine!
　　　　O that some seedling gem,
　　　　Worthy such noble stem,
　Honored and blessed in their shadow might grow!
　　　　Loud should Clan Alpine then
　　　　Ring from the deepmost glen,
　"Roderigh Vich Alpine dhu, ho! ieroe!"

(RODERICK *proudly acknowledges the homage of his men, and dismisses them. He speaks aside with* MALCOLM GRAEME.)

ELLEN. O my father, why did you hunt so far from home? Why have you returned so late?

DOUGLAS. My child, the chase is the only pastime left to the Douglas. It is mere mimicry of noble war, but it is still a gallant pastime. I strayed far east, my Ellen, and I did not stray safe—the King's horsemen scour the country all around.

ELLEN (*aghast*). The King's men?

DOUGLAS (*gravely*). The King boasts to have tamed the Border-side; now he comes hither. I met Malcolm, and, though he is still a royal ward, he risked life and land to bring me here.

(ELLEN *turns to* MALCOLM, *stretching out her hand.* RODERICK *stands with folded arms, frowning.*)

DOUGLAS (*to* MALCOLM). Roderick shall welcome you, despite old spleen, for Douglas's sake. Then you must seek Strath-Endrick Glen, and risk no further peril for me.

RODERICK (*stepping forward*). Short is my speech. I have neither the time nor the temper for flattering words. Kinsman and father; Ellen—why turn away your eyes, cousin?—Graeme—foe or friend, I know not which—the King is in this region. This king, this tyrant of Scotland, has made one sheep-walk of the Lowland dales, where once martial clans rode. What mercy will he have on the Highlands? Douglas—I know you were in Glen Finlas. What is your counsel?

DOUGLAS. I can give poor counsel. I am an exile. The strength of my hand has gone; should I remain here, the royal anger would light upon you. Ellen and I will take refuge in the forest, and dwell there till the stern pursuit on mountain and moor has passed and gone.

RODERICK. No, by mine honor! So help me, heaven, and my good blade! May a curse fall upon the banner of the Pine if it is torn from that of the Bleeding Heart! Hear my blunt speech. Give me your counsel for aid, this maid for wife. So joined, Douglas and Clan Alpine shall foil this faithless, ruthless king. And, when I light my marriage torch, a hundred villages in flames shall scare his slumbers!

(MALCOLM *gazes anxiously at* ELLEN, *who turns as if in fear from* RODERICK, *and looks wildly at her father.*)

DOUGLAS. Roderick, enough! enough! My daughter cannot be your wife. Forgive her. Do not attempt to help us. We will stand or fall together. Nor can I fight against my king. He has wronged me for wrongs done by my kinsman, but, when he was a child, I taught him to ride a horse and wield a sword. I love him still, as I love my own child—and I cannot lift a spear against him.

(RODERICK *looks angry, mortified, and despairing, but he takes the* DOUGLAS's *hand.* ELLEN *turns away, and* MALCOLM *goes to her side.* RODERICK *breaks from the* DOUGLAS *and lays hands on* MALCOLM.)

RODERICK (*furiously*). Back, minion! You can thank only the Douglas and that maid that you are living!

(*They grapple with one another, and* RODERICK *draws his dagger.* DOUGLAS *unsheathes his sword and dashes between them.*)

DOUGLAS.   Chieftains, forgo your rage! The first who strikes is my foe! Madmen! Frantic! What, is the daughter of the Douglas deemed to be the spoil of so dishonorable a strife?

(*They fall apart, sullenly and slowly. Each glares on his rival, with foot advanced, and blade unsheathed.*)

RODERICK (*plunging his dagger in its sheath and speaking scornfully*). Rest safe till morning! It were a pity such a cheek should feel the midnight air! Return then, and tell James Stuart that Roderick and his freeborn clan will never be his lackeys! If he would know more of us, you can show him our strength and our passes. . . . Malise! Give our safe conduct to the Graeme.

MALCOLM (*calmly and boldly*).   You need have no fear—I shall not betray your hold. The place where an angel dwells is sacred, even if it be haunted by robbers. Keep your safe conduct—keep your churlish courtesy for those who are afraid to be your enemies. To me the mountain way is as safe at midnight as at noontide. I owe you nothing, Roderick Dhu—not even the service of a boat. I shall swim across the loch. (*Strips off his plaid*) Brave Douglas, lovely Ellen, I do not say farewell to you. We shall meet again. Chieftain —we too shall find an hour. (*Exit*)

RODERICK (*his hand on his sword*).   We shall find an hour! What, ho, my henchmen! Let the Cross of Fire take its road!

AN ECHO (*within*).   Let the Cross of Fire take its road!

(*Enter* CLANSMEN, MALISE, *and* BRIAN THE HERMIT. BRIAN *makes a heap of juniper, rowan, and oak boughs, to be kindled as a fire. Into this he thrusts one end of the cross, made of yew. The* CLANSMEN *gather about him. He holds the cross high and speaks his curse.*)

BRIAN.

Woe to the clansman, who shall view
This symbol of sepulchral yew,
Forgetful that its branches grew
    Where weep the heavens their holiest dew
        On Alpine's dwelling low!
Deserter of his Chieftain's trust,
He ne'er shall mingle with their dust,
But, from his sires and kindred thrust,

Each clansman's execration just
  Shall doom him wrath and woe!

CLANSMEN (*shaking their swords on high and then striking their shields with them*).

  Woe to the traitor, woe!

BRIAN (*quenching the flame of the cross in the blood of a slaughtered goat*).

When flits this Cross from man to man,
Vich-Alpine's summons to his clan,
Burst be the ear that fails to heed!
Palsied the foot that shuns to speed!
May ravens tear the careless eyes;
Wolves make the coward heart their prize!
As sinks that blood stream in the earth,
So may his heart's blood drench his hearth!
As dies in hissing gore the spark,
Quench thou his light, destruction dark,
And be the grace to him denied,
Bought by this sign to all beside!

CLANSMEN. Woe to the traitor, woe!

RODERICK (*impatiently taking the cross from* BRIAN). Unfurl the curtain of the future world!

BRIAN. Wrapped in the hide of a newly slain bull, I lay on a shelf of a black cliff by the thundering torrent, awaiting my dream. . . .

RODERICK. Your dream? Speak!

BRIAN (*in a solemn, monotonous voice*).
  Which spills the foremost foeman's life,
  That party conquers in the strife!

RODERICK. Be it so. Lanrick Mead is the muster place. The time— instant. (*Giving the cross to* MALISE) Speed, Malise, speed!

CLANSMEN. Speed, Malise, speed!

(*They draw their swords and wave them above their heads.* MALISE *holds the cross high, and stands as if he were about to dash forward with it.*)

ACT III

Scene I. The borders of Loch Katrine.

ELLEN *sits on a stone, her head resting on her hands.* ALLAN-BANE *stands looking out across the lake.*

ALLAN (*turning to* ELLEN). Fear not, dear lady. The Douglas will return —your father will return. He knows that the peril here is too great, and he has gone to prepare a safe retreat for you.

ELLEN (*sadly*). No, no, Allan! I know his purpose. Since you dreamed you saw Malcolm Graeme bound in fetters he has been troubled. He believes that he, the outlaw, is the cause of strife. He has gone to the King of Scotland, to give himself up, to buy my safety.

ALLAN. Nay, dearest Ellen, be sure he's safe—and, for the gallant Graeme, my vision may prove true and yet bode no ill either to you or to him.

(*Enter* FITZ-JAMES. ELLEN *and* ALLAN-BANE *greet him with surprise and alarm.*)

ELLEN. O stranger! what evil chance has brought you here, at such a terrible hour?

FITZ-JAMES. An evil chance! How can it be an evil chance when it lets me look upon you again? (*Kisses her hand*)

ELLEN. But do you not know of *war*—of the battle to be fought—of the guarded pass?

FITZ-JAMES. No, by my faith!

ELLEN (*to* ALLAN-BANE). Go, seek a guide who will lead this knight safely from danger! (*In great distress*) What prompted you to come?

FITZ-JAMES. Sweet Ellen, my life must be precious when you think it worth your care—but I count life nothing to love and honor. Let me speak my purpose at once. I have come to carry you away from these frantic scenes of feud and war. My horses are waiting at Bochastle —they'll carry us to Stirling, and there I will guard you safely.

ELLEN. Say no more, Sir Knight! When you came before, I loved to hear you praise me, and now my vanity has brought you back into the midst of danger. How can I atone for my selfishness? All I can do is tell you the truth. I am an outlaw's daughter. The price of blood is on my father's head. It would be shame to wed me.

FITZ-JAMES. Dearest Ellen——

ELLEN. Still would you speak? Fitz-James, I love a noble youth—who has risked his life for me and mine. Forgive me, be generous, and depart. At the entrance to the pass you will find a guide.

(*He bows in silence, and turns to go. Then he changes his mind, and comes back to her side.*)

FITZ-JAMES (*courteously and sadly*). Hear, lady, a word before I go from you. Once it happened that my poor sword saved the life of the King of Scotland. He gave me this ring, and told me, when I had a boon to ask, to bring it back and make my claim. I am no courtier, Ellen, I live by my lance and my sword, and I have no boon to ask of a prince. Give me your hand. (*Takes it and puts on the ring*) The ring is yours—every king's man knows it. If you are in trouble, seek the King, and claim his pledge to me.

(*Kisses her hand, and exit.* ELLEN *stands looking thoughtfully at the ring.*)

ELLEN (*softly to herself*). Seek the King! I must seek the King!

Scene II. The Trossachs.

A watch-fire burns by a great rock. By it sits RODERICK, *wrapped in his plaid. There is food and a leathern bottle by his side.*

(*Enter* FITZ-JAMES, *his sword drawn.* RODERICK *at once springs to his feet, and stands on guard.*)

RODERICK. Your name and purpose! Saxon, stand!
FITZ-JAMES. A stranger.
RODERICK. What is your need?
FITZ-JAMES. Rest, food, fire, a guide. My guide played me false—I slew him. I have lost my way. I am frozen in this gale.
RODERICK. Are you a friend to Roderick?
FITZ-JAMES. No!
RODERICK. You dare not call yourself his enemy?
FITZ-JAMES. I dare! I am enemy to him and all his murderous band.

(RODERICK *looks at him for a moment, then sheathes his sword.*)

RODERICK.   Bold words! Yet, sure, they speak falsely who say you come here as a secret spy.

FITZ-JAMES.   They do, by heaven! Let me but rest till morning—then let Roderick and the two boldest of his clan face me here, and I write the falsehood on their crests.

RODERICK.   You bear the belt and spur of knight?

FITZ-JAMES.   By these tokens you may recognize the mortal foe of any proud oppressor.

RODERICK.   Enough, enough. Sit down, and share the food and couch of a soldier. (*Gives* FITZ-JAMES *venison, pours out wine, puts fuel on the fire*) Stranger, I am clansman and and kinsman to Roderick Dhu. Each word you speak against his honor demands an avenging stroke. More—much depends on your fate. One blast of my horn, and you would be surrounded. It rests with me to challenge you to stand and measure swords with me, wearied as you are. But not for clan, not for kindred, will I depart from honor's laws. It would be a shame to assail a wearied man, and no stranger must ask hospitality in vain. Rest here till dawn, and I myself will guide you as far as Coilantogle Ford. From thence—your sword must find the way.

FITZ-JAMES (*taking his hand*).   By heaven, I take your courtesy as freely as it is nobly given.

RODERICK.   Rest. The bittern cries—it is night.

(*Spreads out heather, lays his plaid upon it. They unbuckle their swords, lay them down together. Then they lie side by side, and sleep.*)

ACT IV

Scene: Coilantogle Ford.

(*Enter* RODERICK, *followed by* FITZ-JAMES)

RODERICK (*turning to speak with* FITZ-JAMES).   For what strange cause did you seek these wilds? Few dare attempt them without a pass from Roderick Dhu.

FITZ-JAMES (*laying his hand on his sword*).   Brave Gael, my pass hangs in my belt, and by my side. Yet, to speak the truth, when, while hunting, I lost my way here, three days ago, I did not think to use it. All seemed as peaceful and still as the mist on yon mountain. My guide told me that your dangerous chief was far away—though, perchance, the villain lied.

RODERICK. Then why, guessing danger, did you venture again?

FITZ-JAMES. You a warrior, and ask me why? Can we give a fixed cause for our wanderings? Say a flown falcon—a strayed grayhound—a mountain maiden—or, if the path is known to be dangerous, the lure of its danger.

RODERICK. You have heard nought of Lowland war against Roderick?

FITZ-JAMES. No, by my word. Soldiers are mustered to guard the King's sports at Stirling—and I do not doubt that when they know the mountaineer has prepared for war, their banners will no longer hang in Doune but flutter on the field of battle.

RODERICK. May they flutter free! free as Clan Alpine's pine waves! But, stranger, since you came here in peace, why do you so boldly boast yourself the mortal foe of Roderick?

FITZ-JAMES. Warrior, I am bound by promise to match myself with this proud man! Twice have I sought Clan Alpine's glen in peace—when I come again, I come with banners, brands, and bows! (*Speaking passionately and resolutely*) No man ever longed for his heart's desire as I long to see this rebel chieftain and his band before me!

RODERICK. Have then thy wish!

(*He whistles shrilly. Other whistles answer his, wild and shrill. Instantly the* MEN OF CLAN ALPINE, *with swords drawn, spring as if from the earth, and surround* RODERICK, *who stares proudly and haughtily at his enemy.* FITZ-JAMES *sets his back against a rock, draws his sword, and stands ready to defend himself.*)

These are Clan Alpine's warriors! And, Saxon, I am Roderick Dhu!

FITZ-JAMES. Come one, come all! This rock shall flee as soon as I!

RODERICK (*Looks at him with respect and surprise and waves his hand. Instantly his men vanish.* FITZ-JAMES *gazes about him as if wondering if he has been deluded, and again faces* RODERICK). Fear nothing. (*Throws down his target and plaid*) Bold Saxon—Roderick has discharged his trust. He has led you through the pass of danger. Now, man to man, and steel to steel, you shall know his vengeance. Here

I stand before you, with no advantage, armed as you are. This is Coilantogle Ford. From this place your sword alone is your pass.

FITZ-JAMES.   Brave chief, never before have I hesitated to draw my blade. I have sworn your death. Yet—I owe you a deep debt. You have given me life; you have kept fair and generous faith. Can nought but blood atone our feud? Are there no means—

RODERICK (*firmly*).   None, Saxon, none! And hear—to fire your flagging zeal—the Saxon cause depends on your prowess. Thus Fate has spoken:

> Who spills the foremost foeman's life,
> His party conquers in the strife.

FITZ-JAMES.   Then, by my word, that riddle is read! Seek yonder brake beneath the cliff—my treacherous guide, Red Murdoch, lies there, slain by my hand. Yield then to fate, and not to me. Let us go to James at Stirling—and I plight my honor that all shall be well with you.

RODERICK (*proudly and angrily*).   You are so presumptuous because you slew a wretched kern! Do you think that Roderick will do homage to king or to fate? My clansman's blood calls for revenge! Not yet prepared? By heaven, I change my thought. I hold your valor that of some vain carpet knight, who did not deserve my courtesy, whose best boast is to wear a braid of his lady's tresses——

FITZ-JAMES (*furiously*).   I thank you, Roderick, for that word. Now farewell, truce! Begone, pity! We try this quarrel hilt to tilt.

(*Quickly they draw their swords, and throw the scabbards to the ground. They cross swords. Three times* JAMES *touches* RODERICK *with his blade and wounds him slightly. He fights skillfully, using his blade as sword and shield;* RODERICK *violently and clumsily, being obviously wearied and angered by loss of blood. At last* JAMES *forces his sword from his hand, and brings him to his knees.*)

FITZ-JAMES.   Yield, or your heart's blood dyes my blade!

RODERICK.   I defy your threats and your mercy! Let the recreant who fears death yield!

(*He springs treacherously upon* JAMES, *and locks his arms about him.*

They tug and strain and go down, RODERICK's knee planted on JAMES's breast. RODERICK throws back his hair, draws his hand over his eyes to clear them from blood and mist, snatches out his dagger, holds it aloft, and plunges it down to his enemy's breast, but misses his mark, suddenly faint from his wounds. His arm falls lifelessly to the ground, and his fingers relax their hold on the dagger. JAMES rises, and bends over his dying foe.)

FITZ-JAMES *(reverently).* Cold—and lowly laid. Brave warrior—brave spirit, do not scorn my grief.

(Lays his plaid over RODERICK—stands for a moment looking at him —then glances about him, as if suddenly remembering that he is surrounded by enemies, and exits.)

ACT V

Scene: Stirling.

The town is gay with preparations for the games. Now a group with banners, now musicians, now MORRIS DANCERS and masquers pass across the stage. All are laughing and making merry.

(Enter the DOUGLAS)

DOUGLAS. It is true. All my fears are true. The noble Malcolm Graeme is a prisoner; Roderick will soon know the royal vengeance. Only I can ward off their fate. My task is to die for them. . . . *(To a CITIZEN)* Why this quaint array?

CITIZEN. The Stirling games are held today! The King himself comes to see the show!

(Sound of applause coming nearer and nearer)

VOICES OF THE CROWD. The King! The King! Long live the Commons' King, King James!

(Enter the KING, with LEWIS OF TULLIBARDINE and the ROYAL GUARD. Morris dance. The King's SERVANTS throw gold among the dancers. Bugles sound.)

HERALD. Clear the ring for the wrestling!

(*A space is made. Two strong men,* HUGH OF LARBERT *and* JOHN OF ALLOA, *stand forth.*)

HUGH OF LARBERT.   I challenge the mightiest!

JOHN OF ALLOA.   I challenge the mightiest!

DOUGLAS (*suddenly starting forward*).   Then challenge me! I stand for the mightiest.

(*Flourish. They wrestle.* DOUGLAS *overthrows* HUGH OF LARBERT, *who rises and limps slowly and painfully away. After a longer round, he throws* JOHN OF ALLOA, *who is carried away senseless.*)

1ST CITIZEN.   I have seen such strength before in one man only. . . .

2ND CITIZEN.   Such strength lives only in the Douglas blood.

HERALD.   Advance, unknown victor, and take the prize of the wrestling match, the golden ring.

(*Flourish.* DOUGLAS *advances, and the* KING, *giving him his prize, looks coldly at him, and at once turns away. He makes as if to speak, but checks himself, and stands looking disappointed and sad.*)

HERALD.   Men who would show your strength, advance to put the stone!

(YEOMEN *advance, and try to raise a great stone, but cannot move it.* DOUGLAS *bares his arm, stoops, heaves up the stone, and hurls it away. Loud applause.*)

1ST CITIZEN.   A rood beyond the farthest mark!

HERALD.   Advance, unknown victor, and take your prize, a purse of gold.

(*The* KING, *with unmoved look, gives him the purse of gold. The* DOUGLAS *smiles proudly and indignantly, and throws the gold among the crowd.*)

1ST CITIZEN.   Strong of arm!

2ND CITIZEN.   And free of hand!

3RD CITIZEN.   The Douglas arm! The Douglas hand!

4TH CITIZEN.   Douglas of the stalwart hand is an exile!

(*Murmurs rise among the applause: "A Douglas! A Douglas!"* JAMES *signs to one of his* GUARD, *who lays hands on the* DOUGLAS, *who instantly strikes him to the ground. The* GUARD *advance and would seize him, but he draws his sword, raises his hand, and speaks loudly and sternly.)*

DOUGLAS.   Back, back, on your lives, pack of menials! Yes! behold, King James, the Douglas! He offers himself as a willing victim, who comes to crave your grace, not for himself, but for his friends.

KING.   Presumptuous lord! You, James of Bothwell, were the only one of your proud ambitious clan whom I would not recognize as a foe, to whom I showed mercy, as a woman might. But shall a monarch brook your haughty eye and your injurious blows? Break off the sports! Clear the ground! Captains of the guard! Arrest this offender!

(Uproar among the people. The GUARD *surround the* DOUGLAS. *Cries of "A Douglas! The noble Douglas! Rescue him! Break through to him!")*

DOUGLAS *(to one of the soldiers of the* GUARD).   Sir John of Hyndford! it was my sword that laid knighthood on your shoulder! In remembrance of that good deed, let me speak to these misguided men.

(He is allowed to come forward and speak to the people.)

DOUGLAS.   Hear me, gentle friends! If the Douglas suffers without cause, it will not soothe his suffering to know that, for his sake, Scotland has shed the blood of Scotland. Not for the Douglas shall mother lose son, wife husband, child father. Not for the Douglas shall Scotland turn upon herself. Love me still, it is your right—love Scotland first, as I do.

(The turmoil ceases. The DOUGLAS *is led aside, the* SOLDIERS *who guard him walking with trailing spears, as if mourning for him. The* KING *looks at him for a moment, as if his old love for him would overcome his anger; then, with a resolute gesture, he turns and speaks with one of his attendants.)*

(Enter ELLEN *and* ALLAN-BANE. *They walk as if they were weary.)*

LEWIS OF TULLIBARDINE *(jestingly accosting* ELLEN).   Welcome to Stirling, fair maid! Do you come to seek a champion? Does your high quest need a knight? Or may the venture suit a squire?

(Sweeps off his plumed cap and bows as if in mock courtesy.)

ELLEN *(simply and proudly)*.   I crave audience of the King!

LEWIS *(amused)*.   Audience of the *King*, pretty maid?

ELLEN *(showing ring)*.   This signet is the royal pledge—this signet given by the King to James Fitz-James.

LEWIS *(with deep respect)*.   This ring commands my duty. Pardon, lady, my foolish talk. Permit me to conduct you to the King.

(Leads her to the circle where the KING stands. She looks round in bewilderment, clasps her hands, and kneels at his feet. He bends, kisses her brow, and raises her.)

KING.   Yes, fair one, the wandering poor Fitz-James is Scotland's King. Ask what you will—he will redeem his signet.

(She gazes at him as if she could not yet believe the truth.)

KING *(laughing)*.   Still unbelieving! *(Turning to the guarded DOUGLAS)* Lord James of Douglas, confirm this doubting maid.

(ELLEN gives a little cry as she sees her father a prisoner. The DOUGLAS comes forward and takes her in his arms.)

KING *(gently)*.   You need not ask pardon for your father. Wrong had I from his kinsman, not from him. His prince forgives him, if he forgives his prince.

(Holds out his hand to the DOUGLAS, who kneels to kiss it.)

KING *(to ELLEN)*.   You still hold Fitz-James's talisman. What do you seek from the King?

ELLEN.   Pardon for the bold chieftain, who lawless as he was, would have protected my father and me—pardon for Roderick Dhu.

(MALCOLM is brought forward, and kneels before the KING.)

KING *(moved)*.   Alas! That is beyond the King's power. I know his heart. I know his hand. I have shared his cheer, I have proved his sword. I would give my fairest earldom to give him life—but it may not be. Have you no other boon to ask—no other captive friend to save?

(ELLEN, unable to speak, turns to DOUGLAS and gives him the ring.)

KING (*gravely*).   Nay, then, stubborn justice must be done. Captain, bring forth Malcolm Graeme!

KING (*in pretended sternness*).   Rash youth, great has been your fault. You have attempted to shelter an outlaw; you have dishonored your loyal name. (*Looking at* ELLEN) No suppliant sues for you. You must feel the royal vengeance! (*Takes the gold chain from his neck, puts it upon* MALCOLM, *and lays the clasp in* ELLEN's *hand*) Fetters and warder for the Graeme!

(MALCOLM *and* ELLEN *gaze at one another in delight; then turn to the* KING. *Applause from the crowd*)

CURTAIN

How is peace restored to society in this play? What are the obstacles that have to be overcome? How is Ellen similar to the girl in "The Fish and the Ring," to Beauty, and to Lady Mary? Do you think that these innocent heroines may primarily be symbols of what we would *like* to see triumph over the monstrous forces in this world?

What characteristics of the world imagined in the tales in this phase, "The Power of Innocence," are especially desirable? What wishes come true?

WITHDRAWAL
FROM ACTION

In the phase called "Innocence" we read about young people, and gods, who had little or no experience with real evil. In "The Quest" and "The Power of Innocence" we read about a wide variety of adventures in which we saw innocence and virtue encounter monstrous or destructive forces. Now we move into a phase called "Withdrawal from Action." The vigorous adventures have ended here. A mood of contemplation, or of rest, contrasts with the earlier liveliness of battles against various kinds of "monsters."

Song

How sweet I roamed from field to field,
    And tasted all the summer's pride,
'Till I the prince of love beheld,
    Who in the sunny beams did glide!

He showed me lilies for my hair,
    And blushing roses for my brow;
He led me through his gardens fair,
    Where all his golden pleasures grow.

With sweet May dews my wings were wet,
    And Phoebus fired my vocal rage;
He caught me in his silken net,
    And shut me in his golden cage.

He loves to sit and hear me sing,
    Then, laughing, sports and plays with me;
Then stretches out my golden wing,
    And mocks my loss of liberty.

William Blake

What experience did the speaker have that forced him to give up his youthful innocence and freedom? How does he feel about his past?

The speaker has a golden wing, as well as hair and a brow. What creature does the poet metaphorically identify himself with?

What part of this poem could be placed under "Innocence?" Why could the whole poem not be placed there?

The Poetry of Earth

The poetry of earth is never dead;
    When all the birds are faint with the hot sun,
    And hide in cooling trees, a voice will run
From hedge to hedge about the new-mown mead;
That is the Grasshopper's—he takes the lead
    In summer luxury,—he has never done
    With his delights; for when tired out with fun
He rests at ease beneath some pleasant weed.
The poetry of earth is ceasing never:
    On a lone winter evening, when the frost
        Has wrought a silence, from the stove there shrills
The Cricket's song, in warmth increasing ever,
    And seems to one in drowsiness half lost,
        The Grasshopper's among some grassy hills.

John Keats

The grasshopper and the cricket are active in this poem, but the poet speaks of himself as "half lost" in drowsiness. What does the cricket's song make him think about on a winter evening as he drowses by the fire? What *is* the poetry of earth?

Village in Late Summer

Lips half-willing in a doorway.
Lips half-singing at a window.
Eyes half-dreaming in the walls.
Feet half-dancing in a kitchen.
Even the clocks half-yawn the hours
And the farmers make half-answers.

Carl Sandburg

How does Sandburg suggest a near-paralysis of action in this village in late summer? What mental picture do you receive from each of the six lines?

A Soft November Night

Trees in this November night
Are leafed with light
From street lamps or the moon,
And you shall soon
Walk from the city to the wood
Where stood your birthplace, centuries
And centuries ago.

How can November thus
Be summer? summer fabulous?
While soft as a feather, soft as snow,
Or snowy moonlight on moonlit eaves
One cricket weaves the winds together.

Sleep, you are there.
Sleep, you are home.
The moonlight comb
Combs your hair.
And now you are home.
After centuries, now.
After centuries, home.

Robert Hillyer

What is the birthplace in the wood that the "you" of this poem returns to? What does the poet mean when he says that the moonlight combs the hair of the one returning home? Why does the return to the wood take centuries? Who do you think the "you" is meant to be?

Could this poem be used as an ending for any of the selections in the phase called "The Quest"?

When You Are Old

When you are old and gray and full of sleep,
And nodding by the fire, take down this book,
And slowly read, and dream of the soft look
Your eyes had once, and of their shadows deep;

How many loved your moments of glad grace,
And loved your beauty with love false or true,
But one man loved the pilgrim soul in you,
And loved the sorrows of your changing face;

And bending down beside the glowing bars,
Murmur, a little sadly, how Love fled
And paced upon the mountains overhead
And hid his face amid a crowd of stars.

William Butler Yeats

What scene is imagined here? Who is the person in it, and what is she to do? What has she experienced in the past? What has the speaker experienced? What is the poem's mood?

In "Margaret," in the phase called "Innocence," we have images of early morning, of a child, and of wild wishes. List the images from the poems in this phase, "Withdrawal from Action," that contrast with those three images from "Margaret."

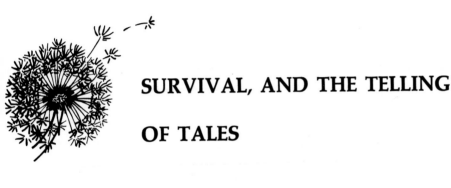

SURVIVAL, AND THE TELLING OF TALES

Captain Murderer

In the following account, a writer remembers a tale of horror that his nurse used to tell him when he was a child. She claimed that it was the only thing that could save him from a weird supernatural being called "The Black Cat."

The first diabolical character who intruded himself on my peaceful youth (as I called to mind that day at Dullborough), was a certain Captain Murderer. This wretch must have been an offshoot of the Blue Beard family, but I had no suspicion of the consanguinity in those times. His warning name would seem to have awakened no general prejudice against him, for he was admitted into the best society and possessed immense wealth. Captain Murderer's mission was matrimony, and the gratification of a cannibal appetite with tender brides. On his marriage morning, he always caused both sides of the way to church to be planted with curious flowers; and when his bride said, "Dear Captain Murderer, I never saw flowers like these before: what are they called?" he answered, "They are called garnish for house lamb," and laughed at his ferocious practical joke in a horrid manner, disquieting the minds of the noble bridal company, with a very sharp show of teeth, then displayed for the first time. He made love in a coach and six, and married in a coach and twelve, and all his horses were milk-white horses with one red spot on the back which he caused to be hidden by the harness. For, the spot *would* come there, though every horse was milk-white when Captain Murderer bought him. And the spot was young bride's blood. (At this terrific point I am indebted for my first personal experience of a shudder and cold beads on the forehead.) When Captain Murderer had made an end of feasting and revelry, and had dismissed the noble guests, and was alone with his wife on the day a month after their marriage, it was his whimsical custom to produce a golden rolling pin and a silver pie board. Now, there was this special feature in the Captain's courtships, that he always asked if the young lady could make pie crust; and if she couldn't by nature or education, she was taught. Well. When the bride saw Captain Murderer produce the golden rolling-pin and silver pie board, she remembered this, and turned up her laced-silk sleeves to make a pie. The Captain brought out a silver pie dish of immense capacity, and the Captain brought out flour and butter and eggs and all things needful, except the inside of the pie; of materials for the staple of the pie itself, the Captain brought out none. Then said the lovely bride, "Dear Captain Murderer, what pie is this to be?" He replied, "A meat pie." Then said the lovely bride, "Dear Captain Murderer, I see no meat." The Captain humorously retorted, "Look in the glass." She looked in the glass, but still she saw no meat, and then the Captain roared with laughter, and suddenly frowning and drawing his sword, bade her roll out the crust. So she rolled out the crust, dropping large tears upon it all the time because he was so cross, and when she had lined the dish with crust and had cut the crust all ready to fit the top, the Captain called out, "*I* see the meat in the glass!" And the bride looked up at the glass, just in time to see the Captain cutting her head off; and he chopped her in pieces, and peppered her, and salted her, and put her in the pie, and sent it to the baker's, and ate it all, and picked the bones.

Captain Murderer went on in this way, prospering exceedingly, until he came to choose a bride from two twin sisters, and at first didn't know which to choose. For, though one was fair and the other dark, they were both equally beautiful. But the fair twin loved him, and the dark twin hated him, so he chose the fair one. The dark twin would have prevented the marriage if she could, but she couldn't; however, on the night before it, much suspecting Captain Murderer, she stole out and climbed his garden wall, and looked in at his window through a chink in the shutter, and saw him having his teeth filed sharp. Next day she listened all day, and heard him make his joke about the house lamb. And that day a month, he had the paste rolled out, and cut the fair twin's head off, and chopped her in pieces, and peppered her, and salted her, and put her in the pie, and sent it to the baker's, and ate it all, and picked the bones.

Now, the dark twin had had her suspicions much increased by the filing of the Captain's teeth, and again by the house-lamb joke. Putting all things together when he gave out that her sister was dead, she divined the truth, and determined to be revenged. So, she went up to Captain Murderer's house, and knocked at the knocker and pulled at the bell, and when the Captain came to the door, said: "Dear Captain Murderer, marry me next, for I always loved you and was jealous of my sister." The Captain took it as a compliment, and made a polite answer, and the marriage was quickly arranged. On the night before it, the bride again climbed to his window, and again saw him having his teeth filed sharp. At this sight she laughed such a terrible laugh at the chink in the shutter, that the Captain's blood curdled, and he said: "I hope nothing has disagreed with me!" At that, she laughed again, a still more terrible laugh, and the shutter was opened and search made, but she was nimbly gone, and there was no one. Next day they went to church in a coach and twelve, and were married. And that day a month, she rolled the pie crust out, and Captain Murderer cut her head off, and chopped her in pieces, and peppered her, and salted her, and put her in the pie, and sent it to the baker's, and ate it all, and picked the bones.

But before she began to roll out the paste she had taken a deadly poison of a most awful character, distilled from toads' eyes and spiders' knees; and Captain Murderer had hardly picked her last bone, when he began to swell, and to turn blue, and to be all over spots, and to scream. And he went on swelling and turning bluer, and being more all over spots and screaming, until he reached from floor to ceiling and from wall to wall; and then, at one o'clock in the morning, he blew up with a loud explosion. At the sound of it, all the milk-white horses in the stables broke their halters and went mad, and then they galloped over everybody in Captain Murderer's house (beginning with the family blacksmith who had filed his teeth) until the whole were dead, and then they galloped away.

Hundreds of times did I hear this legend of Captain Murderer in my early youth, and added hundreds of times was there a mental compulsion upon me in bed, to peep in at his window as the dark twin peeped, and to revisit his horrible house, and look at him in his blue and spotty and screaming stage, as he reached from floor to ceiling and from wall to wall. The young woman who brought me acquainted with Captain Murderer had a fiendish enjoyment of my terrors, and used to begin, I remember—as a sort of introductory overture—by clawing the air with both hands, and uttering a long low hollow groan. So acutely did I suffer from this ceremony in combination with this infernal Captain, that I sometimes used to plead I thought I was hardly strong enough and old enough to hear the story again just yet. But she never spared me one word of it, and indeed commended the awful chalice to my lips as the only preservative known to science against "The Black Cat"—a weird and glaring-eyed supernatural Tom, who was reputed to prowl about the world by night, sucking the breath of infancy, and who was endowed with a special thirst (as I was given to understand) for mine.

Charles Dickens

In "Captain Murderer" devilish crimes and innocent victims are remembered with pleasure, on the whole, because the writer's experiences on hearing about them are now safely in the past. What images does he use to make his tale horrific for his readers? Do you think that he enjoys re-creating a sense of horror?

What selection in the phase called "The Power of Innocence" does "Captain Murderer" remind you of? How is the telling of that tale different from the telling of "Captain Murderer"?

"If I Forget Thee, Oh Earth..."

When Marvin was ten years old, his father took him through the long, echoing corridors that led up through Administration and Power, until at last they came to the uppermost levels of all and were among the swiftly growing vegetation of the Farmlands. Marvin liked it here: it was fun watching the great, slender plants creeping with almost visible eagerness toward the sunlight as it filtered down through the plastic domes to meet them. The smell of life was everywhere, awakening inexpressible longings in his heart: no longer was he breathing the dry, cool air of the residential levels, purged of all smells but the faint tang of ozone. He wished he could stay here for a little while, but Father would not let him. They went onward until they had reached the entrance to the Observatory, which he had never visited: but they did not stop, and Marvin knew with a sense of rising excitement that there could be only one goal left. For the first time in his life, he was going Outside.

There were a dozen of the surface vehicles, with their wide balloon tires and pressurized cabins, in the great servicing chamber. His father must have been expected, for they were led at once to the little scout car waiting by the huge circular door of the airlock. Tense with expectancy, Marvin settled himself down in the cramped cabin while his father started the motor and checked the controls. The inner door of the lock slid open and then closed behind them: he heard the roar of the great air pumps fade slowly away as the pressure dropped to zero. Then the "Vacuum" sign flashed on, the outer door parted, and before Marvin lay the land which he had never yet entered.

He had seen it in photographs, of course: he had watched it imaged on television screens a hundred times. But now it was lying all around him, burning beneath the fierce sun that crawled so slowly across the jet-black sky. He stared into the west, away from the blinding splendor of the sun—and there were the stars, as he had been told but had never quite believed. He gazed at them for a long time, marveling that anything could be so bright and yet so tiny. They were intense unscintillating points, and suddenly he remembered a rhyme he had once read in one of his father's books:

> Twinkle, twinkle, little star,
> How I wonder what you are.

Well, *he* knew what the stars were. Whoever asked that question must have been very stupid. And what did they mean by "twinkle"? You could see at a glance that all the stars shone with the same steady, unwavering light. He abandoned the puzzle and turned his attention to the landscape around him.

They were racing across a level plain at almost a hundred miles an hour, the great balloon tires sending up little spurts of dust behind them. There was no sign of the Colony: in the few minutes while he had been gazing at the stars, its domes and radio towers had fallen below the horizon. Yet there were other indications of man's presence, for about a mile ahead Marvin could see the curiously-shaped structures clustering round the head of a mine. Now and then a puff of vapor would emerge from a squat smokestack and would instantly disperse.

They were past the mine in a moment: Father was driving with a reckless and exhilarating skill as if—it was a strange thought to come into a child's mind—he were trying to escape from something. In a few minutes they had reached the edge of the plateau on which the Colony had been built. The ground fell sharply away beneath them in a dizzying slope whose lower stretches were lost in shadow. Ahead, as far as the eye could reach, was a jumbled wasteland of craters, mountain ranges, and ravines. The crests of the mountains, catching the low sun, burned like islands of fire in a sea of darkness: and above them the stars still shone as steadfastly as ever.

There could be no way forward—yet there was. Marvin clenched his fists as the car edged over the slope and started the long descent. Then he saw the barely visible track leading down the mountainside, and relaxed a little. Other men, it seemed, had gone this way before.

Night fell with a shocking abruptness as they crossed the shadow line and the sun dropped below the crest of the plateau. The twin searchlights sprang into life, casting blue-white bands on the rocks ahead, so that there was scarcely need to check their speed. For hours they drove through valleys and past the foot of mountains whose peaks seemed to comb the stars, and sometimes they emerged for a moment into the sunlight as they climbed over higher ground.

And now on the right was a wrinkled, dusty plain, and on the left, its ramparts and terraces rising mile after mile into the sky, was a wall of mountains that marched into the distance until its peaks sank from sight below the rim of the world. There was no sign that men had ever explored this land, but once they passed the skeleton of a crashed rocket, and beside it a stone cairn surmounted by a metal cross.

It seemed to Marvin that the mountains stretched on forever: but at last, many hours later, the range ended in a towering, precipitous headland that rose steeply from a cluster of little hills. They drove down into a shallow valley that curved in a great arc toward the far side of the mountains: and as they did so, Marvin slowly realized that something very strange was happening in the land ahead.

The sun was now low behind the hills on the right: the valley before them should be in total darkness. Yet it was awash with a cold white radiance that came spilling over the crags beneath which they were driving. Then, suddenly, they were out in the open plain, and the source of the light lay before them in all its glory.

It was very quiet in the little cabin now that the motors had stopped. The only sound was the faint whisper of the oxygen feed and an occasional metallic crepitation as the outer walls of the vehicle radiated away their heat. For no warmth at all came from the great silver crescent that floated low above the far horizon and flooded all this land with pearly light. It was so brilliant that minutes passed before Marvin could accept its challenge and look steadfastly into its glare, but at last he could discern the outlines of continents, the hazy border of the atmosphere, and the white islands of cloud. And even at this distance, he could see the glitter of sunlight on the polar ice.

It was beautiful, and it called to his heart across the abyss of space. There in that shining crescent were all the wonders that he had never known—the hues of sunset skies, the moaning of the sea on pebbled shores, the patter of falling rain, the unhurried benison of snow. These and a thousand others should have been his rightful heritage, but he knew them only from the books and ancient records, and the thought filled him with the anguish of exile.

Why could they not return? It seemed so peaceful beneath those lines of marching cloud. Then Marvin, his eyes no longer blinded by the glare, saw that the portion of the disk that should have been in darkness was gleaming faintly with an evil phosphorescence: and he remembered. He was looking upon the funeral pyre of a world—upon the radioactive aftermath of Armageddon. Across a quarter of a million miles of space, the glow of dying atoms was still visible, a perennial reminder of the ruinous past. It would be centuries yet before that deadly glow died from the rocks and life could return again to fill that silent, empty world.

And now Father began to speak, telling Marvin the story which until this moment had meant no more to him than the fairy tales he had once been told. There were many things he could not understand: it was impossible for him to picture the glowing, multi-colored pattern of life on the planet he had never seen. Nor could he comprehend the forces that had destroyed it in the end, leaving the Colony, preserved by its isolation, as the sole survivor. Yet he could share the agony of those final days, when the Colony had learned at last that never again would the supply ships come flaming down through the stars with gifts from home. One by one the radio stations had ceased to call: on the shadowed globe the lights of the cities had dimmed and died, and they were alone at last, as no men had ever been alone before, carrying in their hands the future of the race.

Then had followed the years of despair, and the long-drawn battle for survival in this fierce and hostile world. That battle had been won, though barely: this little oasis of life was safe against the worst that Nature could do. But unless there was a goal, a future toward which it could work, the Colony would lose the will to live, and neither machines nor skill nor science could save it then.

So, at last, Marvin understood the purpose of this pilgrimage. He would never walk beside the rivers of that lost and legendary world, or listen to the thunder raging above its softly rounded hills. Yet one day— how far ahead?—his children's children would return to claim their heritage. The winds and the rains would scour the poisons from the burning lands and carry them to the sea, and in the depths of the sea they would waste their venom until they could harm no living things. Then the great ships that were still waiting here on the silent, dusty plains could lift once more into space, along the road that led to home.

That was the dream: and one day, Marvin knew with a sudden flash of insight, he would pass it on to his own son, here at this same spot with the mountains behind him and the silver light from the sky streaming into his face.

He did not look back as they began the homeward journey. He could not bear to see the cold glory of the crescent Earth fade from the rocks around him, as he went to rejoin his people in their long exile.

Arthur C. Clarke

Where, in space and time, are Marvin and his father? How is this science fiction tale also a story of pilgrimage? What is the purpose of the journey taken here? What images are used to describe the area through which the scout car moves?

What tales will Marvin be passing on to his children? What effect will the tales have on the small group of exiles?

Notice how the events in this story take place at the extreme opposite point in imagined time from the selections in the first phase, "Beginnings." Think back over the stories and poems in this First Story. In which ones does the action primarily look toward some future time? Which ones look back to a rich or experience-filled past?

All That's Past

Very old are the woods;
    And the buds that break
Out of the briar's boughs,
    When March winds wake,
So old with their beauty are—
    Oh, no man knows
Through what wild centuries
    Roves back the rose.

Very old are the brooks;
    And the rills that rise
Where snow sleeps cold beneath
    The azure skies
Sing such a history
    Of come and gone,
Their every drop is as wise
    As Solomon.

Very old are we men;
    Our dreams are tales
Told in dim Eden
    By Eve's nightingales;
We wake and whisper awhile,
    But, the day gone by,
Silence and sleep like fields
    Of amaranth lie.

Walter de la Mare

What point in time does this poem describe? Is there any suggestion of a future? What knowledge does nature possess? Why is Eden "dim"? What tales are dreamed of by the old men of stanza three?

The Old Men Admiring
Themselves in the Water

I heard the old, old men say,
"Everything alters,
And one by one we drop away."
They had hands like claws, and their knees
Were twisted like the old thorn-trees
By the waters.
I heard the old, old men say,
"All that's beautiful drifts away
Like the waters."

William Butler Yeats

What do the "old, old men" talk of? Do they have any hope of returning to an earlier, better time? In which lyric—this one or "All That's Past"—is there an expression of bitterness or disillusionment?

How do the images here, of the clawed and twisted old men, make the images of the new creation in the first phase of this Story seem very remote?

After the Flood, We

We must be the only ones
left, in the mist that has risen
everywhere as well
as in these woods

I walk across the bridge
toward the safety of high ground
(the tops of the trees are like islands)

gathering the sunken
bones of the drowned mothers
(hard and round in my hands)
while the white mist washes
around my legs like water;

fish must be swimming
down in the forest beneath us,
like birds, from tree to tree
and a mile away
the city, wide and silent,
is lying lost, far undersea.

You saunter beside me, talking
of the beauty of the morning,
not even knowing
that there has been a flood,

tossing small pebbles
at random over your shoulder
into the deep thick air,

not hearing the first stumbling
footsteps of the almost-born
coming (slowly) behind us,
not seeing
the almost-human
brutal faces forming
(slowly)
out of stone.

Margaret Atwood

In this poem only two human beings have survived a great Flood that has destroyed an earlier creation. Only one of them appears to have any knowledge of the world that has been lost. What is it about the speaker's awareness of their surroundings that creates a sense of menace?

What connections do you see between this monologue and Arthur Clarke's story?

How does this poem take you back to "Beginnings"? Why wouldn't it fit there? What is the difference between "first" creatures and "survivors"?

You might try writing a science fiction tale, on the pattern of Clarke's story. Pretend that you are one of the survivors of the Flood in Atwood's poem. What kind of a past do you remember? What tales will you pass on to your children? What caused the catastrophe, and how will you deal with the almost-human faces forming out of stones?

This poem and Yeats's poem about the old men point to a kind of literature that is different from what we have been reading in the First Story. Their images of loss and fear suggest a second kind of Story, where beauty and innocence will be overcome. Try to trace the growing presence of evil in the selections that make up the First Story. Then try listing the images of innocence, goodness, and beauty here.

ROMANCE

When you look at a picture, you can do so in any or all of three ways. You can stand close to the painting and notice tiny details, such as the artist's brush strokes. You can stand back a little way and "read" what the picture tells you about the actual world of real people and things. Or, you can stand even further back and see the structure of the picture in terms of geometric shapes. A work of literature can also be studied in these three ways. In the individual selections of this first chapter there is much fascinating detail; some of the questions have invited you to examine that detail. In addition, you have been aware that the selections, to some extent, tell you about things and events in the real world. If, finally, you have "stood back" a little, you have seen overall shapes and structures as well.

All stories may be seen as having "shapes." Stories move in either of two directions. We may have an upward movement, from an unfortunate situation to a better one, as for example when the girl in "The Fish and the Ring" is freed from being a lowly servant and made a prince's bride. In such a story, what we feel should happen *does* happen, and the story takes on a "comic" (or happy) shape. In contrast, we may find a downward movement, when the characters fall from good fortune into a bad situation, as for example when Marvin's father in "If I Forget Thee, Oh Earth . . ." is trapped on the moon, unable to get back to an atomically-polluted earth. In such a story, what we feel *should* happen is frustrated, and the story takes on a "tragic" (or sad) shape.

When you have read all the individual selections which go to make up this First Story, think about it structurally, that is, stand just far enough back to see the whole of it. You will be aware of three facts. First, various kinds of literature have been mixed together here (biblical passages, lyric poems, folk tales, myths, autobiography, and science fiction). Second, some of the selections were originally written as part of larger works (the Bible passages, for example). Third, other selections were written as separate items (most of the short poems, obviously). But whether fragments of larger works or independent items, these pieces of literature have been fitted into particular places in this First Story in order to allow you to "stand back" and see the "shape" or structure of a basic story pattern.

In a broad sense, then, the material you have just read is divided into six phases. Each selection in each phase can be read and thought about as something interesting in itself. It also tells us something about real life. But if we stand back we can see that all the individual pieces have been arranged so that they form the shape of a particular kind of story, which we call a romantic one.

"Beginnings" tells how all things in the world began, in innocence and splendor. This section also shows us the beginning of a heroic life. "Innocence" presents us with figures who still are part of the world of innocence, although some of them, even the child Margaret in Sandburg's lyric, are pressing toward experiences and adventures. "The Quest" shows us the various motives and goals that send human beings out into different kinds of adventures, mental or spiritual ones as well as physical. Like "The Quest," "The Power of Innocence" also shows innocent heroes and heroines. These people too are pitted against evil forces, but here the emphasis is on the fact that it is their innocence that helps them "come through" successfully. In "Withdrawal from Action" we read about a time when vigorous adventures have ended. Here a new mood of contemplation, or inactivity and rest, contrasts with the earlier liveliness of battle against various kinds of "monsters." Finally, in "Survival, and the Telling of Tales," the great romantic adventures become material for the memory, for nostalgic story-telling. De la Mare, for example, thinks back to the "tales/Told in dim Eden." But in our last two poems, describing the bitter old men and the survivors of the Flood, this romantic past has faded almost entirely away. Now we get a new, realistic sense of all-too-real, unromantic facts.

The men and women who inhabit the pages of romance are nearly always human beings, but they are not particularly realistic. The heroes are often idealized almost to the point of divinity:

Jack overcomes Death; Finn performs superhuman deeds. Even when the "hero" is not a human but an animal, he can also be godlike, like Coyote, who miraculously saves his people by killing the Kamiah monster. These characters live in a simpler world than the actual one which exists outside our imagination. In this imagined world, magic often has real power. There may be evil in this world to threaten its well-being, but the "good" people normally are successfully defended against this evil. Basically, romance expresses what most people, at least in one part of their minds and emotions, wish would happen. We see this daydreaming aspect in the mind of the boy in Singer's "To the Wild Cows." The boy himself is not idealized, but he "romanticizes" his world.

The desirable imagined world of romance is peopled by brave heroes, like Finn and Jack, and by beautiful heroines, like Ellen and Beauty. The characters of romance are simplified. They are either made extraordinarily good (like Beauty) or very villainous (like Mr. Fox). The villains in romance represent the undesirable world of cruel stepsisters and false parents, of evil magicians and witches, of tyrants and ogres. This evil world is often a twisted or distorted imitation of the good one. We have an example of this in "Captain Murderer," where the traditional bridal feast takes the form of cannibalism. Human figures, then, are sharply contrasted in romance. The same is true of the animal kingdom. The evil animals are monsters, beasts of prey, serpents, and dragons. The good animals are lambs, dogs, or horses. Often the good animals in romance are to some extent supernatural or fabulous, like the loving, devoted simurgh in "The Story of Zal" or Coyote in "The Kamiah Monster."

The plot of romance involves adventures. The most important adventure is the quest, which has three main stages: the perilous journey or exile, the struggle, and the glorification of the hero or heroine. This quest often involves dragon- or monster-killing. The monster may be a beast (the Kamiah monster or Aillen of the Flaming Breath) or it may be something or someone dragonish or monstrous (the Bloody Chamber in "Mr. Fox" or the monstrous Mr. Fox himself). Various rewards are possible for the successful hero or heroine. Buried treasure, called a hoard, is one. Power and wisdom are others. A beautiful bride or handsome husband is yet another. In Yeats's lyric "The Song of Wandering Aengus," a "glimmering girl" and the "silver apples of the moon" and "golden apples of the sun" will keep Aengus wandering and searching throughout his whole life.

Nowadays romance is not much in fashion with most writers, but it can be found in fragmentary form in the story line of many advertising commercials. For example, some advertisements show a desirable world of idealized, beautiful young women who always seem to win idealized, handsome young men. The suggestion deliberately being made is that drinking the right kind of soft drink will guarantee beauty, endless youth, good times, and also fulfillment in love. The romance plot can also be found today in "western" films, where the cowboy is remarkably like a medieval knight, complete with faithful horse, trusty weapon, and morals superior to those of the villains who are threatening the good homesteaders or the beautiful schoolteacher. This similarity is not surprising when we realize that romance in each period of history expresses the ideals of the society it springs from. A North American frontier society created romantic frontier tales. A space-age society transfers the romantic frontier to outer space and other planets. A modern state undergoing revolutionary changes develops tales glorifying revolutionary heroes who are pitted against established systems.

The romance story is one of the great narrative patterns man has devised. Romances vary widely in their subject matter and in the different codes of values expressed in them. Some of the romance heroes you have just read about are more "realistic" than others. The Bronzeville man in the prize fight arena is a good deal more realistic than Finn but he is still a romantic hero who fights his own kind of dragon. As you think back over the gathering of literature in our First Story, you will realize that the poems and prose works found here are only a small sample of this kind of writing. Romance is literature in which man expresses his dreams of a world where wishes can come true and an original paradise, now lost, can be restored. The dream is of a world where the light shines on in the dark and everything *is* very good.

SECOND STORY

DESTRUCTION OF THE BEAUTIFUL

Crystal Moment

Once or twice this side of death
Things can make one hold his breath.

From my boyhood I remember
A crystal moment of September.

A wooded island rang with sounds
Of church bells in the throats of hounds.

A buck leaped out and took the tide
With jewels flowing past each side.

With his high head like a tree
He swam within a yard of me.

I saw the golden drop of light
In his eyes turned dark with fright.

I saw the forest's holiness
On him like a fierce caress.

Fear made him lovely past belief,
My heart was trembling like a leaf.

He leaned toward the land and life
With need upon him like a knife.

In his wake the hot hounds churned,
They stretched their muzzles out and yearned.

They bayed no more, but swam and throbbed,
Hunger drove them till they sobbed.

Pursued, pursuers reached the shore
And vanished. I saw nothing more.

So they passed, a pageant such
As only gods could witness much,

Life and death upon one tether
And running beautiful together.

Robert P. Tristram Coffin

What is the theme or main idea of the poem?

Look at the poem's images. Which are similes (which of them say that one thing is *like* another)? Which are metaphors (which of them directly identify one thing as another, different one)?

The Coming of Connla

This is a legend from ancient Ireland,
about the hero Cuchulain (koo•hoo'lin).

For a long time after the fight at the ford and the death of Ferdia, for a long while after the wounds of his body were healed, it was as though Cuchulain were wounded in his mind; he had no joy left to him even in hunting, no joy in harp song, nor in the touch of Emer's hands. But little by little, as the months passed into years, that wound also healed, though maybe the scar of it never quite ceased its aching, and he returned to his old ways. The fire of life burned high in him again, and he answered as of old to the call of any adventure that came his way.

And many and many were the adventures that came, and if they did not come, he went out to seek them. Once he even went down into Tir-Nan-Og, the Land of Youth, to fight for Labraid of the Quick Sword, among the Fairy Kind. That was the time he met with Fand, who was wife to Manannan the Lord of the Sea, and loved her from one new moon until the next. For always he was quick to fall in love, but always he forgot the new love in a while and a while, and came back to Emer as a man comes again to his own hearth after a day's hunting. And that time too, he came back to her, and she waiting as she had learned to wait until he chose to come, among the apple trees of Dun Dealgan.

It was many years now since his warrior training, and Cuchulain would have forgotten Aifa of the Golden Hair as completely as the others that came after, save that, as time passed and Emer bore him no child, he would wonder now and then, when he saw the boys at hurley, whether he had a son growing up for him somewhere away beyond the Land of Shadows. And at such times Emer would know what was in his mind, and it would be to her as though a small sharp dagger were turning in her heart.

And then one summer day, when King Conor Mac Nessa and some of his lords had been racing their horses together on the hard white wave-rippled sand of the coast below Dun Dealgan they beheld, coming in to shore, a little boat that lifted and dipped gull-wise into the troughs of the waves. It was sheathed in plates of bronze instead of dressed skins; and in it sat a boy with gilded oars in his hands, and his head shone in the sunlight and dancing water-light, more golden than the oars. There was a small pile of stones in the boat, and ever and again as the King and his nobles watched, the boy would fit a stone into his sling and cast at one of the sea birds that swooped and circled overhead, and always he cast in such a way that he did not kill the bird but brought it down alive to his feet; and then he would take it up and caress it, and cast it back none the worse into the blue air. And all kinds of other strange and fantastic things he did, showing off joyously for the watching men on the shore.

But Conor shook his head that was beginning to be gray streaked like a badger, watching still as the boat came into the shallows, and he said, "If the grown men of that boy's country were to come against us they would grind us as the quern stone grinds barley. Woe to any land into which that boy shall come, for when he is grown to manhood it is in my mind that no land will be large enough to hold him!" And as the keel ran up on to the white sand, he said to Cethern Son of Findtan, who stood beside him, "Go you and bid him turn back along the sea trail by which he came."

But when Cethern delivered the King's word, the boy only laughed and tossed up his head like a high-spirited colt, and said, "Surely here is a poor welcome for a stranger! But I will not turn back for you."

"It is not my word, but the King's," Cethern said.

And the boy replied, "Then I will not turn back for the King, nor for any man!"

So Cethern returned to the King and told him what the boy had said.

Then Conor Mac Nessa turned to Conall of the Victories. "Go you and see if you can make my message clearer—also something sharper if need be."

So Conall drew his leaf-shaped bronze sword and strode into the shallows, but the boy saw him coming and fitted a stone into his sling and let fly at him with a high triumphant shout; and the wind of the sling stone passing by his cheek knocked Conall down, and before he could rise again, spitting out salt water, the boy was upon him and had wrenched his arms behind his back and bound them with his own shield strap.

Then the King, more certain than ever of the danger that lay in a boy of such powers, sent another of his champions to demand where he came from, and another and another; and each as he came, the boy treated as he had treated Conall of the Victories.

When upward of a score of the Red Branch Warriors had suffered in the same way, the King spoke again urgently to Cethern Mac Findtan. "Ride to Dun Dealgan and bring me back Cuchulain to do battle against this boy whom even Conall of the Victories is powerless to overcome."

So Cethern mounted his horse and rode to Dun Dealgan a few miles off, in a smother of blown dune sand.

Cuchulain was in the women's chambers with Emer his wife when the King's summons reached him, and he would have caught up his weapons and gone at once in answer, but Emer swept up from the cushioned bench on which she had been sitting at her embroidery frame, and caught him by the arm. "Cuchulain, let you not go!"

He looked at her, and the laughter flashed up in the sad face of him. "Not go, when the King summons?"

"You are ill," Emer said quickly. "Only a while since you were complaining of pain in your head. It is in my mind that you should go to bed now, and I will send word to the King for you."

"Emer, you say foolish things. There is no pain in my head. Why should I not go?"

"I do not know, but there is a shadow on me, and it comes from you. . . . It is in my mind that the son Aifa promised you might be just such a one as this boy!"

Cuchulain reached for his sword to belt it on, and she saw that he meant to go for all that; and she clung round his neck as she had used to do in their first years together. "Listen, my Hound, do not you go out to the King, for the fear is in me that if you do, it may be to slay your own son!"

But Cuchulain kissed her and pulled her arms away. "Ach now, leave be, my girl; the King sends for me to do battle with this stranger, and though it be young Connla himself, I must slay him if need be, for the honor of Ulster."

"Honor!" cried Emer, and the eyes of her flashing battle sparks. "Always this talk of honor with you men! It is more to you than truth, more than love; you must be forever slaying each other and being slain; and what is it to your lordly selves, the hearts of the women you break behind you?"

"It was not so you spoke when I came wooing you under the apple trees, Emer."

"I was a little green hard apple—I have learned somewhat since those days—I might have been the boy's mother."

But Cuchulain scarcely heard her, for he had gone striding to the door and was calling for Laeg to yoke his chariot.

And when it was done, and the horses brought trampling round into the forecourt, he sprang in and taking the reins himself, as he often did when he did not need his hands for spear and shield, he drove out after Cethern Mac Findtan.

They followed the coast until they came to the stretch of hard white sand, and there they found the King and his hearth companions standing with their horses and looking on with a grim air of waiting, some of them cherishing wounds or the red weals of their lately loosed bonds, while the boy, seemingly as fresh as in the moment when he sprang ashore, stood at the surf's edge, tossing up his throw-spears in shining arcs and making them spin in the sunshine like whirling lesser suns, to amuse himself and pass the time.

Cuchulain sprang down from the chariot, and bidding Laeg to wait with the rest, he strolled forward alone. "That is a pretty play that you make with your weapons, child; do they teach all the babes to play so, in the land that you come from?"

"Only to those that are not cross-eyed," said the boy, laughing. "For the game has its hazards," and he sent the spear again spinning skyward, and caught it when the down-wheeling point was within a finger's breadth of Cuchulain's breast.

"That was neatly done at all events," said Cuchulain, who had not moved. "Tell me now, who you are and what place you come from."

"That is a thing that I may not tell." The boy let the spear rest quiet now, in his hand.

"No man who sets foot within the borders of Ulster and refuses to tell either his name or the place whence he comes is likely to be living long afterward."

"That's as may be," said the boy. "Still I may not tell."

"Then best be making ready to die with it untold."

"I am ready," said the boy; and with the words scarcely spoken they sprang together in the shallows. For a while they fought with their swords, so that the sparks flew up from the blades on the sea wind, as the salt spray flew about their legs. And Cuchulain knew that he had met one whose sword play matched his own, and his heart leapt in the fierce joy of equal combat, until the boy with a swift outward flick of the wrist, delicately shored off a lock of his dark flying hair.

Then Cuchulain laughed sharp in his throat, and flung his sword away back to the sand behind him. "That is enough of blade play between you and me," and leapt upon the boy like a mountain cat. And the boy sent his own sword spinning in the same way and sprang on to a low slab of rock near by in the surf that gave surer foothold than the shifting sand; and there they grappled together, each struggling with his bare hands to throw the other, but the boy planted his feet so strongly that they sank deep into the rock—for which reason, that place was called the Strand of the Footprints ever after—and for all his mighty strength, Cuchulain could not shift him a hair's breadth.

Long and long they fought, as when two mighty stags battle for the lordship of the herd; until at last even they began to weary, their footing grew less firm-gripped to the rock, and suddenly with a cry and a clanging of war gear and a slipping and slithering splash, they went down locked together into the foam-laced shallows. But the boy fell uppermost and his arms were still fast about Cuchulain, and his knee on Cuchulain's chest, holding him down. The Champion was near to drowning, and then, at his final gasp, with fire in his breast and the blood roaring in his ears and his eyes full of a dazzling darkness, he heard, very dimly, a shout from the shore, and something flew humming toward where they threshed about. With a supreme effort he tore one arm free, and reaching out, caught the shaft of a great spear that came like a long tailed fish cleaving the bright boil of water above him; and the instant his hand closed on it, he knew that Laeg had flung him the Gae Bolg. Struggling half over, he drew back his arm and made the death thrust. And he felt—the sick memory on him—how it tore into the boy's belly as it had done into Ferdia's by the ford, and all the shallows about them were red with blood.

"That is a thing that Skatha never trained me to," cried the boy. "And I am hurt—I am hurt——"

And Cuchulain slipped clear of the slight body and lifted him and laid him across the rock; and so saw on his hand the gold ring that he had given to Aifa, fifteen summers ago.

He gathered the boy in his arms and carried him out of the shallows and laid him down on the white sand before Conor and the Lords of Ulster. "Here is Connla my son for you," he said, gray and cold. "There is little enough that Ulster or Ulster's honor has to fear from him now, my Lord the King."

"Is that the King?" the boy asked faintly, for the life was still in him.

"That is Conor Mac Nessa, your kinsman, and the King," Cuchulain said, kneeling to support him.

"If I had five years to grow to manhood among your warriors, we would conquer the world, to the very—gates of Rome and—beyond." And he looked up into his father's face as though already from a long way away. "But since the thing is as it is, my father, let you point out to me the famous champions that are here; for often I have thought of the Champions of the Red Branch, and I would see them before I go."

So one after another the Red Branch Warriors came to kneel beside him and speak their names, and then the boy said, "So: my heart is glad that I have seen great men, and it is time that I must be away," and turned his face against his father's shoulder and cried out once, small and plaintive like a newborn child, and the life was gone from him.

The men of Ulster dug his grave in the coarse grass, under the rest-harrow and frilled yellow sea poppies of the shore, and set up his pillar stone with deep mourning.

That was the second and the last time in all his life that Cuchulain used the Gae Bolg; and the first time he slew his dearest friend with it, and the second time he slew his only son.

Retold by Rosemary Sutcliff

What destroys Connla? Is Connla in some way like the stag in the poem that opens this phase?

When he is dying, Connla says, "But since the thing is as it is . . ." What kind of human attitude does this symbolize?

The hero Finn, in "How Finn Won His Father's Place," is very much like Connla. Both are young, high-born, handsome, and brave. What is the main difference between their stories?

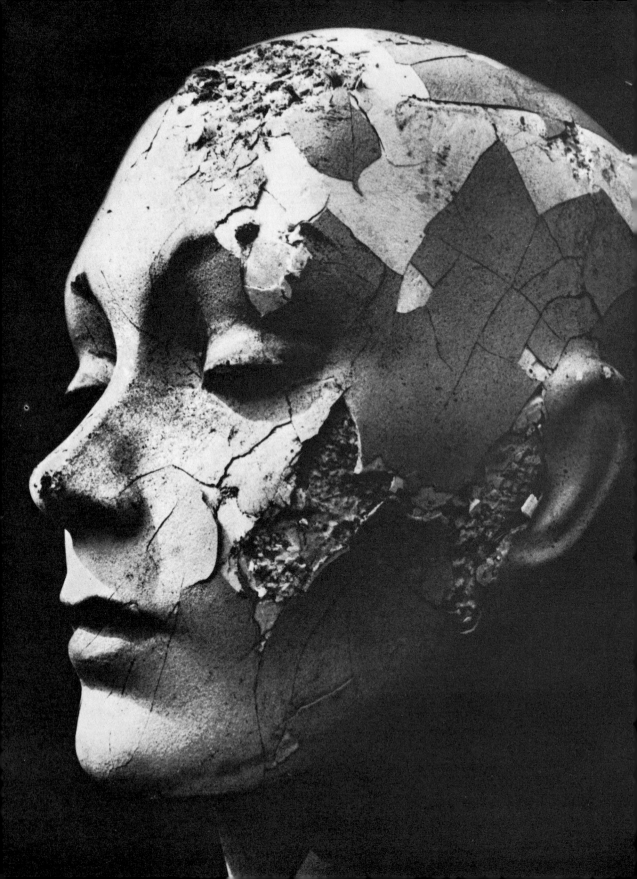

Lucy Gray

Oft I had heard of Lucy Gray:
    And, when I crossed the wild,
I chanced to see at break of day
    The solitary child.

No mate, no comrade Lucy knew;
    She dwelt on a wide moor,
The sweetest thing that ever grew
    Beside a human door!

You yet may spy the fawn at play,
    The hare upon the green;
But the sweet face of Lucy Gray
    Will never more be seen.

"Tonight will be a stormy night,
    You to the town must go;
And take a lantern, Child, to light
    Your mother through the snow."

"That, Father, will I gladly do:
    'Tis scarcely afternoon—
The minster-clock has just struck two,
    And yonder is the moon!"

At this the father raised his hook
    And snapped a faggot-band;
He plied his work; and Lucy took
    The lantern in her hand.

Not blither is the mountain roe:
    With many a wanton stroke
Her feet disperse the powdery snow,
    That rises up like smoke.

The storm came on before its time:
    She wandered up and down;
And many a hill did Lucy climb:
    But never reached the town.

The wretched parents all that night
    Went shouting far and wide;
But there was neither sound nor sight
    To serve them for a guide.

At daybreak on a hill they stood
    That overlooked the moor;
And thence they saw the bridge of wood,
    A furlong from their door.

They wept—and, turning homeward, cried,
    "In heaven we all shall meet!"
When in the snow the mother spied
    The print of Lucy's feet.

Then downward from the steep hill's edge
    They tracked the footmarks small;
And through the broken hawthorn hedge,
    And by the long stone wall;

And then an open field they crossed:
    The marks were still the same;
They tracked them on, nor ever lost;
    And to the bridge they came.

They followed from the snowy bank
    Those footmarks, one by one,
Into the middle of the plank;
    And further were there none!

Yet some maintain that to this day
    She is a living child;
That you may see sweet Lucy Gray
    Upon the lonesome wild.

O'er rough and smooth she trips along,
    And never looks behind;
And sings a solitary song
    That whistles in the wind.

William Wordsworth

In this ballad an innocent girl is a victim of natural forces. How is she seen as a child of nature? Did this girl need nature? Did nature need the girl?

Why, if Lucy drowned, would some maintain that she is still a "living child"?

Autumn Movement

I cried over beautiful things knowing no beautiful thing lasts.

The field of cornflower yellow is a scarf at the neck of the copper sunburned woman, the mother of the year, the taker of seeds.

The northwest wind comes and the yellow is torn full of holes, new beautiful things come in the first spit of snow on the northwest wind, and the old things go, not one lasts.

Carl Sandburg

The experience of the "crystal moment" in Coffin's poem makes the poet hold his breath. In "Autumn Movement" the poet says he cried. What do the poets realize that makes them react in these ways? What is the effect of each lyric on you?

What poem near the end of the First Story also expresses the idea that no beautiful thing lasts?

There are four victims in this first phase of our Story. What do they have in common? What forces destroy them?

THE DEATH OF INNOCENCE

Autumn in Jail

In autumn a friend
Sent in an apple.
I made to eat it
All at once.
Red: too red.

In my palm, heavy:
Heavy as the world.

Tsuboi Shigeji

The Fall

The serpent was more crafty than any wild creature that the Lord God had made. He said to the woman, "Is it true that God has forbidden you to eat from any tree in the garden?" The woman answered the serpent, "We may eat the fruit of any tree in the garden, except for the tree in the middle of the garden; God has forbidden us either to eat or to touch the fruit of that; if we do, we shall die." The serpent said, "Of course you will not die. God knows that as soon as you eat it, your eyes will be opened and you will be like gods knowing both good and evil." When the woman saw that the fruit of the tree was good to eat, and that it was pleasing to the eye and tempting to contemplate, she took some and ate it. She also gave her husband some and he ate it. Then the eyes of both of them were opened and they discovered that they were naked; so they stitched fig-leaves together and made themselves loincloths.

The man and his wife heard the sound of the Lord God walking in the garden at the time of the evening breeze and hid from the Lord God among the trees of the garden. But the Lord God called to the man and said to him, "Where are you?" He replied, "I heard the sound as you were walking in the garden, and I was afraid because I was naked, and I hid myself." God answered, "Who told you that you were naked? Have you eaten from the tree which I forbade you?" The man said, "The woman you gave me for a companion, she gave me fruit from the tree and I ate it." Then the Lord God said to the woman, "What is this that you have done?" The woman said, "The serpent tricked me, and I ate." Then the Lord God said to the serpent:

> "Because you have done this you are accursed
> more than all cattle and all wild creatures.
> On your belly you shall crawl, and dust you shall eat
> all the days of your life.
> I will put enmity between you and the woman,
> between your brood and hers.
> They shall strike at your head,
> and you shall strike at their heel."

To the woman he said:

"I will increase your labor and your groaning,
and in labor you shall bear children.
You shall be eager for your husband,
and he shall be your master."

And to the man he said:

"Because you have listened to your wife
and have eaten from the tree which I forbade you,
accursed shall be the ground on your account.
With labor you shall win your food from it
all the days of your life.
It will grow thorns and thistles for you,
none but wild plants for you to eat.
You shall gain your bread by the sweat of your brow
until you return to the ground;
for from it you were taken.
Dust you are, to dust you shall return."

The man called his wife Eve because she was the mother of all who live. The Lord God made tunics of skins for Adam and his wife and clothed them. He said, "The man has become like one of us, knowing good and evil; what if he now reaches out his hand and takes fruit from the tree of life also, eats it and lives for ever?" So the Lord God drove him out of the garden of Eden to till the ground from which he had been taken. He cast him out, and to the east of the garden of Eden he stationed the cherubim and a sword whirling and flashing to guard the way to the tree of life.

Genesis 3, 1–24

How do Adam and Eve lose their innocence?

In what way is their life to be different, after they have been cursed by God? Why are they kept from the tree of life by a flaming sword?

Eve in Reflection

Painful and brief the act. Eve on the barren shore
Sees every cherished feature, plumed tree, bright grass,
Fresh spring, the beasts as placid as before
Beneath the inviolable glass.

There the lost girl gone under sea
Tends her undying grove, never raising her eyes
To where on the salt shell beach in reverie
The mother of all living lies.

The beloved face is lost from sight,
Marred in a whelming tide of blood:
And Adam walks in the cold night
Wilderness, waste wood.

Jay Macpherson

There are two Eves in this poem. The Eve who is on the shore is "the mother of all living." (See why Adam called his wife "Eve" in the biblical account of the Fall.) The Eve reflected in the water is "the lost girl," that is, the innocent Eve of Paradise. The brief but painful act that "separated" the two Eves was the eating of the apple.

In this lyric the word *reflection* refers both to a mirror image in the water and to reflective thought about something now past. What images tell you about the kind of world Eve and Adam now inhabit? How does it differ from the earlier one they knew, the one now lost beneath the sea? Whose face is lost from sight, and why is it "beloved"?

Spring and Fall: *To a Young Child*

Márgarét, are you gríeving
Over Goldengrove unleaving?
Leáves, líke the things of man, you
With your fresh thoughts care for, can you?
Áh! ás the heart grows older
It will come to such sights colder
By and by, nor spare a sigh
Though worlds of wanwood leafmeal lie;
And yet you wíll weep and know why.
Now no matter, child, the name:
Sórrow's spríngs áre the same.
Nor mouth had, no nor mind, expressed
What heart heard of, ghost guessed:
It ís the blight man was born for,
It is Margaret you mourn for.

Gerard Manley Hopkins

The poet is punning, or playing with words, when he says that Golden-grove is "unleaving." What does the word mean? Why would Margaret grieve over falling leaves? What does the phrase "fresh thoughts" suggest about Margaret's age? What change does the poet predict for her?

Does the title tell you anything about the meaning of the poem?

What is the "blight man was born for"? Is the answer found in the biblical selection called "The Fall"?

What connections can you find between this Margaret and Sandburg's Margaret in the First Story?

Refugee in America

There are words like *Freedom*
Sweet and wonderful to say.
On my heart-strings freedom sings
All day everyday.

There are words like *Liberty*
That almost make me cry.
If you had known what I knew
You would know why.

Langston Hughes

Not Poor, Just Broke

I never learned hate at home, or shame. I had to go to school for that. I was about seven years old when I got my first big lesson. I was in love with a little girl named Helene Tucker, a light-complected little girl with pigtails and nice manners. She was always clean and she was smart in school. I think I went to school then mostly to look at her. I brushed my hair and even got me a little old handkerchief. It was a lady's handkerchief, but I didn't want Helene to see me wipe my nose on my hand. The pipes were frozen again, there was no water in the house, but I washed my socks and shirt every night. I'd get a pot, and go over to Mister Ben's grocery store, and stick my pot down into his soda machine. Scoop out some chopped ice. By evening the ice melted to water for washing. I got sick a lot that winter because the fire would go out at night before the clothes were dry. In the morning I'd put them on, wet or dry, because they were the only clothes I had.

Everybody's got a Helene Tucker, a symbol of everything you want. I loved her for her goodness, her cleanness, her popularity. She'd walk down my street and my brothers and sisters would yell, "Here comes Helene," and I'd rub my tennis sneakers on the back of my pants and wish my hair wasn't so nappy and the white folks' shirt fit me better. I'd run out on the street. If I knew my place and didn't come too close, she'd wink at me and say hello. That was a good feeling. Sometimes I'd follow her all the way home, and shovel the snow off her walk and try to make friends with her Momma and her aunts. I'd drop money on her stoop late at night on my way back from shining shoes in the taverns. And she had a Daddy, and he had a good job. He was a paper hanger.

I guess I would have gotten over Helene by summertime, but something happened in that classroom that made her face hang in front of me for the next twenty-two years. When I played the drums in high school it was for Helene and when I broke track records in college it was for Helene and when I started standing behind microphones and heard applause I wished Helene could hear it, too. It wasn't until I was twenty-nine years old and married and making money that I finally got her out of my system. Helene was sitting in that classroom when I learned to be ashamed of myself.

It was on a Thursday. I was sitting in the back of the room, in a seat with a chalk circle drawn around it. The idiot's seat, the troublemaker's seat.

The teacher thought I was stupid. Couldn't spell, couldn't read, couldn't do arithmetic. Just stupid. Teachers were never interested in finding out that you couldn't concentrate because you were so hungry, because you hadn't had any breakfast. All you could think about was noontime, would it ever come? Maybe you could sneak into the cloakroom and steal a bite of some kid's lunch out of a coat pocket. A bite of something. Paste. You can't really make a meal of paste, or put it on bread for a sandwich, but sometimes I'd scoop a few spoonfuls out of the paste jar in the back of the room. Pregnant people get strange tastes. I was pregnant with poverty. Pregnant with dirt and pregnant with smells that made people turn away, pregnant with cold and pregnant with shoes that were never bought for me, pregnant with five other people in my bed and no Daddy in the next room, and pregnant with hunger. Paste doesn't taste too bad when you're hungry.

The teacher thought I was a troublemaker. All she saw from the front of the room was a little black boy who squirmed in his idiot's seat and made noises and poked the kids around him. I guess she couldn't see a kid who made noises because he wanted someone to know he was there.

It was on a Thursday, the day before the Negro payday. The eagle always flew on Friday. The teacher was asking each student how much his father would give to the Community Chest. On Friday night, each kid would get the money from his father, and on Monday he would bring it to the school. I decided I was going to buy me a Daddy right then. I had money in my pocket from shining shoes and selling papers, and whatever Helene Tucker pledged for her Daddy I was going to top it. And I'd hand the money right in. I wasn't going to wait until Monday to buy me a Daddy.

I was shaking, scared to death. The teacher opened her book and started calling out names alphabetically.

"Helene Tucker?"

"My Daddy said he'd give two dollars and fifty cents."

"That's very nice, Helene. Very, very nice indeed."

That made me feel pretty good. It wouldn't take too much to top that. I had almost three dollars in dimes and quarters in my pocket. I stuck my hand in my pocket and held onto the money, waiting for her to call my name. But the teacher closed her book after she called everybody else in the class.

I stood up and raised my hand.

"What is it now?"

"You forgot me."

She turned toward the blackboard. "I don't have time to be playing with you, Richard."

"My Daddy said he'd . . ."

"Sit down, Richard, you're disturbing the class."

"My Daddy said he'd give . . . fifteen dollars."

She turned around and looked mad. "We are collecting this money for you and your kind, Richard Gregory. If your Daddy can give fifteen dollars you have no business being on relief."

"I got it right now, I got it right now, my Daddy gave it to me to turn in today, my Daddy said . . ."

"And furthermore," she said, looking right at me, her nostrils getting big and her lips getting thin and her eyes opening wide, "we know you don't have a Daddy."

Helene Tucker turned around, her eyes full of tears. She felt sorry for me. Then I couldn't see her too well because I was crying, too.

"Sit down, Richard."

And I always thought the teacher kind of liked me. She always picked me to wash the blackboard on Friday, after school. That was a big thrill, it made me feel important. If I didn't wash it, come Monday the school might not function right.

"Where are you going, Richard?"

I walked out of school that day, and for a long time I didn't go back very often. There was shame there.

Now there was shame everywhere. It seemed like the whole world had been inside that classroom, everyone had heard what the teacher had said, everyone had turned around and felt sorry for me. There was shame in going to the Worthy Boys Annual Christmas Dinner for you and your kind, because everybody knew what a worthy boy was. Why couldn't they just call it the Boys Annual Dinner, why'd they have to give it a name? There was shame in wearing the brown and orange and white plaid mackinaw the welfare gave to 3,000 boys. Why'd it have to be the same for everybody so when you walked down the street the people could see you were on relief? It was a nice warm mackinaw and it had a hood, and my Momma beat me and called me a little rat when she found out I stuffed it in the bottom of a pail full of garbage way over on Cottage Street. There was shame in running over to Mister Ben's at the end of the day and asking for his rotten peaches, there was shame in asking Mrs. Simmons for a spoonful of sugar, there was shame in running out to meet the relief truck. I hated that truck, full of food for you and your kind. I ran into the house and hid when it came. And then I started to sneak through alleys, to take the long way home so the people going into White's Eat Shop wouldn't see me. Yeah, the whole world heard the teacher that day, we all know you don't have a Daddy.

Dick Gregory

This is an autobiographical account of actual experiences that the author had in his boyhood. How does this sentence affect him: "We are collecting this money for you and your kind, Richard Gregory."?

The teacher only sees a boy squirming in her classroom. What does Richard Gregory do to show that he feels he is more than that?

What does he mean when he says "Everybody's got a Helene Tucker..."?

How was Dick Gregory's youthful experience with the adult world different from the youthful experience described in "To the Wild Cows" in the First Story?

David

I

David and I that summer cut trails on the Survey,
All week in the valley for wages, in air that was steeped
In the wail of mosquitoes, but over the sunalive week-ends
We climbed, to get from the ruck of the camp, the surly

Poker, the wrangling, the snoring under the fetid
Tents, and because we had joy in our lengthening coltish
Muscles, and mountains for David were made to see over,
Stairs from the valleys and steps to the sun's retreats.

II

Our first was Mount Gleam. We hiked in the long afternoon
To a curling lake and lost the lure of the faceted
Cone in the swell of its sprawling shoulders. Past
The inlet we grilled our bacon, the strips festooned

On a poplar prong, in the hurrying slant of the sunset.
Then the two of us rolled in the blanket while round us the
    cold
Pines thrust at the stars. The dawn was a floating
Of mists till we reached to the slopes above timber, and won

To snow like fire in the sunlight. The peak was upthrust
Like a fist in a frozen ocean of rock that swirled
Into valleys the moon could be rolled in. Remotely unfurling
Eastward the alien prairie glittered. Down through the dusty

Skree[1] on the west we descended, and David showed me
How to use the give of shale for giant incredible
Strides. I remember, before the larches'[2] edge,
That I jumped a long green surf of juniper flowing

[1] **skree:** slope covered with loose stones.

[2] **larches:** pine trees.

Away from the wind, and landed in gentian and saxifrage
Spilled on the moss. Then the darkening firs
And the sudden whirring of water that knifed down a
    fern-hidden
Cliff and splashed unseen into mist in the shadows.

III

One Sunday on Rampart's arête [1] a rainsquall caught us,
And passed, and we clung by our blueing fingers and
    bootnails,
An endless hour in the sun, not daring to move
Till the ice had steamed from the slate. And David taught me

How time on a knife-edge can pass with the guessing of
    fragments
Remembered from poets, the naming of strata beside one,
And matching of stories from schooldays . . . We crawled
    astride
The peak to feast on the marching ranges flagged

By the fading shreds of the shattered stormcloud. Lingering
There it was David who spied to the south, remote,
And unmapped, a sunlit spire on Sawback, an overhang
Crooked like a talon. David named it the Finger.

That day we chanced on the skull and the splayed white ribs
Of a mountain goat underneath a cliff, caught tight
On a rock. Around were the silken feathers of kites.
And that was the first I knew that a goat could slip.

IV

And then Inglismaldie. Now I remember only
The long ascent of the lonely valley, the live
Pine spirally scarred by lightning, the slicing pipe
Of invisible pika, and great prints, by the lowest

[1] **arête:** ridge.

Snow, of a grizzly. There it was too that David
Taught me to read the scroll of coral in limestone
And the beetle-seal in the shale of ghostly trilobites,
Letters delivered to man from the Cambrian waves.

V

On Sundance we tried from the col [1] and the going was hard.
The air howled from our feet to the smudged rocks
And the papery lake below. At an outthrust we balked
Till David clung with his left to a dint in the scarp,[2]

Lobbed the iceax over the rocky lip,
Slipped from his hold and hung by the quivering pick,
Twisted his long legs up into space and kicked
To the crest. Then, grinning, he reached with his freckled
    wrist

And drew me up after. We set a new time for that climb.
That day returning we found a robin gyrating
In grass, wing-broken. I caught it to tame but David
Took and killed it, and said, "Could you teach it to fly?"

VI

In August, the second attempt, we ascended the Fortress.
By the Forks of the Spray we caught five trout and fried
    them
Over a balsam fire. The woods were alive
With the vaulting of mule-deer and drenched with clouds
    all the morning,

Till we burst at noon to the flashing and floating round
Of the peaks. Coming down we picked in our hats the bright.
And sunhot raspberries, eating them under a mighty
Spruce, while a marten moving like quicksilver scouted us.

[1] col: pass.

[2] scarp: face of a cliff.

VII

But always we talked of the Finger on Sawback, unknown
And hooked, till the first afternoon in September we slogged
Through the musky woods, past a swamp that quivered
    with frog-song,
And camped by a bottle-green lake. But under the cold

Breath of the glacier sleep would not come, the moonlight
Etching the Finger. We rose and trod past the feathery
Larch, while the stars went out, and the quiet heather
Flushed, and the skyline pulsed with the surging bloom

Of incredible dawn in the Rockies. David spotted
Bighorns across the moraine [1] and sent them leaping;
With yodels the ramparts redoubled and rolled to the peaks,
And the peaks to the sun. The ice in the morning thaw

Was a gurgling world of crystal and cold blue chasms,
And seracs [2] that shone like frozen salt-green waves.
At the base of the Finger we tried once and failed. Then
    David
Edged to the west and discovered the chimney; the last

Hundred feet we fought the rock and shouldered and kneed
Our way for an hour and made it. Unroping we formed
A cairn on the rotting tip. Then I turned to look north
At the glistening wedge of giant Assiniboine, heedless

Of handhold. And one foot gave. I swayed and shouted.
David turned sharp and reached out his arm and steadied me,
Turning again with a grin and his lip ready
To jest. But the strain crumbled his foothold. Without

A gasp he was gone. I froze to the sound of grating
Edge-nails and fingers, the slither of stones, the lone
Second of silence, the nightmare thud. Then only
The wind and the muted beat of unknowing cascades.

---

[1] **moraine:** accumulation of earth and stones deposited by a glacier.

[2] **seracs:** pinnacles of ice.

VIII

Somehow I worked down the fifty impossible feet
To the ledge, calling and getting no answer but echoes
Released in the cirque,[1] and trying not to reflect
What an answer would mean. He lay still, with his lean

Young face upturned and strangely unmarred, but his legs
Splayed beneath him, beside the final drop,
Six hundred feet sheer to the ice. My throat stopped
When I reached him, for he was alive. He opened his gray

Straight eyes and brokenly murmured, "Over . . . over"
And I, feeling beneath him a cruel fang
Of the ledge thrust in his back, but not understanding,
Mumbled stupidly, "Best not to move," and spoke

Of his pain. But he said, "I can't move. . . . If only I felt
Some pain." Then my shame stung the tears to my eyes
As I crouched, and I cursed myself, but he cried
Louder, "No, Bobbie! Don't ever blame yourself.

I didn't test my foothold." He shut the lids
Of his eyes to the stare of the sky, while I moistened his lips
From our water flask and tearing my shirt into strips
I swabbed the shredded hands. But the blood slid

From his side and stained the stone and the thirsting lichens,
And yet I dared not lift him up from the gore
Of the rock. Then he whispered, "Bob, I want to go over!"
This time I knew what he meant and I grasped for a lie

And said, "I'll be back here by midnight with ropes
And men from the camp and we'll cradle you out." But I
     knew
That the day and the night must pass and the cold dews
Of another morning before such men unknowing

[1] cirque: natural amphitheater.

The ways of mountains could win to the chimney's top.
And then, how long? And he knew . . . and the hell of hours
After that, if he lived till we came, roping him out.
But I curled beside him and whispered, "The bleeding will
    stop.

You can last." He said only, "Perhaps . . . For what? A
    wheelchair,
Bob?" His eyes brightening with fever upbraided me.
I could not look at him more and said, "Then I'll stay
With you." But he did not speak, for the clouding fever.

I lay dazed and stared at the long valley,
The glistening hair of a creek on the rug stretched
By the firs, while the sun leaned round and flooded the ledge,
The moss, and David still as a broken doll.

I hunched to my knees to leave, but he called and his voice
Now was sharp with fear. "For Christ's sake, push me over!
If I could move . . . or die. . . ." The sweat ran from his
    forehead,
But only his head moved. A kite was buoying

Blackly its wings over the wrinkled ice.
The purr of a waterfall rose and sank with the wind.
Above us climbed the last joint of the Finger
Beckoning bleakly the wide indifferent sky.

Even then in the sun it grew cold lying there. . . . And I knew
He had tested his holds. It was I who had not. . . . I looked
At the blood on the ledge, and the far valley. I looked
At last in his eyes. He breathed, "I'd do it for you, Bob."

IX

I will not remember how nor why I could twist
Up the wind-devilled peak, and down through the chimney's
    empty
Horror, and over the traverse alone. I remember
Only the pounding fear I would stumble on It

When I came to the grave-cold maw of the bergschrund [1]...
    reeling
Over the sun-cankered snowbridge, shying the caves
In the névé [2] ... the fear, and the need to make sure It was
    there
On the ice, the running and falling and running, leaping

Of gaping green-throated crevasses, alone and pursued
By the Finger's lengthening shadow. At last through the
    fanged
And blinding seracs I slid to the milky wrangling
Falls at the glacier's snout, through the rocks piled huge

On the humped moraine, and into the spectral larches,
Alone. By the glooming lake I sank and chilled
My mouth but I could not rest and stumbled still
To the valley, losing my way in the ragged marsh.

I was glad of the mire that covered the stains, on my ripped
Boots, of his blood, but panic was on me, the reek
Of the bog, the purple glimmer of toadstools obscene
In the twilight. I staggered clear to a firewaste, tripped

And fell with a shriek on my shoulder. It somehow eased
My heart to know I was hurt, but I did not faint
And I could not stop while over me hung the range
Of the Sawback. In blackness I searched for the trail by the
    creek,

And found it. . . . My feet squelched a slug and horror
Rose again in my nostrils. I hurled myself,
Down the path. In the woods behind some animal yelped.
Then I saw the glimmer of tents and babbled my story.

[1] **bergschrund:** deep crevice.

[2] **névé:** hardened snow of a glacial region.

I said that he fell straight to the ice where they found him,
And none but the sun and incurious clouds have lingered
Around the marks of that day on the ledge of the Finger,
That day, the last of my youth, on the last of our mountains.

Earle Birney

What incidents and omens foreshadow David's tragedy? What sentence indicates the climax of the tragic action in this narrative poem? Why does Bob say that the day of the accident was the last of his youth?

Bob has to make his way back down the mountain to camp with the knowledge of how his friend died. How do some of the images in this last part of the poem reinforce a sense of horror and "deadness"? If we say that these images also suggest a repugnant, hell-like world, what images in the first part of the poem suggest an opposite, "good" world, a pleasant paradise?

The Trees They Do Grow High

With movement—not too slow

"The trees they do grow high, and the leaves they do grow green, But the time is gone and past, my love,____ that you and I have seen. It's a cold win - ter's night, my love, and here I must a - bide a - lone. My bon - ny lad was young, but a - grow - ing."____

2 / "O, Father, dearest Father, I fear you've done me wrong,
   For you've married me to a bonny boy, but I fear he is too
      young."
   "O, my daughter, dearest daughter, if you stay at home a time
      with me,
   A lady you shall be, while he's growing.

3 / "We'll send him to a college for a year or two,
   And then perhaps in time, my love, into a man he'll grow.
   I will buy you a ribbon blue to tie about his bonny waist,
   To let the ladies know that he's married."

4 / At the age of sixteen, he was a married man,
   And at the age of seventeen, he was father of a son,
   And at the age of eighteen, his grave it was a-growing green,
   And that did put an end to his growing.

5 / She made her love a shroud of the holland, O so fine,
   And ev'ry stitch she put in it, her tears came trickling down.
   "O, once I had a sweetheart, but now I have got never a one,
   So fare you well, my true love, for ever.

6 / "The trees they do grow high and the leaves they do grow
      green,
   But the time is gone and past, my love, that you and I have
      seen.
   It's a cold winter's night, my love, and here I must
      abide alone.
   So fare you well, my true love, for ever."

What puts an end to the boy's growing? What happens to the trees?
How does the young widow connect the trees with her husband?

This song does not describe a death of innocence so much as the
death of an innocent. Discuss.

The Demon Lover

"O where have you been, my long, long love,
    This long seven years and more?"
"O I'm come to seek my former vows
    Ye granted me before."

"O hold your tongue of your former vows,
    For they will breed sad strife;
O hold your tongue of your former vows,
    For I am become a wife."

He turned him right and round about,
    And the tear blinded his eye:
"I would never have trodden on Irish ground,
    If it had not been for thee.

"I might have had a king's daughter,
    Far, far beyond the sea;
I might have had a king's daughter,
    Had it not been for love o' thee."

"If ye might have had a king's daughter,
    Yer self ye had to blame;
Ye might have taken the king's daughter,
    For ye knew that I was none.

"If I was to leave my husband dear,
    And my two babes also,
O what have you to take me to,
    If with you I should go?"

"I have seven ships upon the sea—
    The eighth brought me to land—
With four-and-twenty bold mariners,
    And music on every hand."

She has taken up her two little babes,
    Kissed them both cheek and chin:
"O fare ye well, my own two babes,
    For I'll never see you again."

She set her foot upon the ship,
    No mariners could she behold;
But the sails were o' the taffeta,
    And the masts o' the beaten gold.

They had not sailed a league, a league,
    A league but barely three,
When dismal grew his countenance,
    And troubled grew his eye.

They had not sailed a league, a league,
    A league but barely three,
Until she espied his cloven foot,
    And she wept right bitterly.

"O hold your tongue of your weeping," says he,
    "Of your weeping now let me be;
I will show you how lilies grow
    On the banks of Italy."

"O what hills are yon, yon pleasant hills,
    That the sun shines sweetly on?"
"O yon are the hills of heaven," he said,
    "Where you will never win."

"O what mountain is yon," she said,
    "All so dreary with frost and snow?"
"O yon is the mountain of hell," he cried,
    "Where you and I will go."

He struck the top-mast with his hand,
    The fore-mast with his knee,
And he broke that gallant ship in twain,
    And sank her in the sea.

Is it fair that the woman in this ballad should end up going to the frost- and snow-covered mountain of hell rather than to the pleasant hills of heaven?

Do you see any connection between this ballad and the story of the fall of Eve, in Genesis 3?

The Butcher Boy

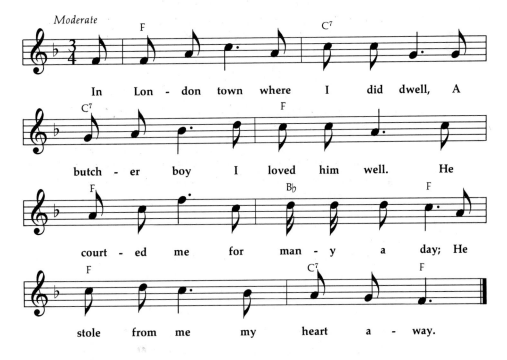

Moderate

In Lon - don town where I did dwell, A butch - er boy I loved him well. He court - ed me for man - y a day; He stole from me my heart a - way.

2 / There is an inn in that same town,
And there my love he sits him down;
He takes a strange girl on his knee
And tells her what he wouldn't tell me.

3 / The reason is, I'll tell you why,
Because she's got more gold than I.
But gold will melt and silver fly,
And in time of need be as poor as I.

4 / I'll go upstairs and make my bed.
"There is nothing to do," my mother said.
My mother she has followed me,
Saying, "What is the matter, my daughter dear?"

5 / "O mother dear, you little know
What pains or sorrow or what woe!
Go get a chair and sit me down,
With pen and ink I'll write all down."

6 / She wrote a letter, she wrote a song,
She wrote a letter, she wrote it long;
On every line she dropped a tear,
At every verse cried, "Willy dear!"

7 / Her father he came home that night
Inquiring for his heart's delight;
He went upstairs, the door he broke,
He found her hanging on a rope.

8 / He took a knife and cut her down,
And in her bosom these lines he found:
"O what a foolish girl was I
To hang myself for a butcher's boy.

9 / "Go dig my grave both wide and deep,
Put a marble stone at my head and feet,
And on my grave place a turtle dove
To show the world that I died for love."

This girl was baffled by a bad experience of adult life. How was it like the experience of young Dick Gregory in the story "Not Poor, Just Broke"? How do the endings differ?

Fall, Leaves, Fall

Fall, leaves, fall; die, flowers, away;
Lengthen night and shorten day;
Every leaf speaks bliss to me
Fluttering from the autumn tree.

I shall smile when wreaths of snow
Blossom where the rose should grow;
I shall sing when night's decay
Ushers in a drearier day.

Emily Brontë

What season or seasons of the year have been associated with grief and bitterness in this Second Story? What different feelings are usually associated with the "green" or springtime world? Why would someone (like Emily Brontë in this poem) welcome the loss of the "green" world of innocence?

Star and Dead Leaves

A star was talking with the withered leaves
In the still midnight.
Only the wind stirred round me then.
Strangely forlorn,
I tried to share their words.

The star swooped from the heavens.

I searched among dead leaves
But could not ever find it.

Tsuboi Shigeji

Why was the poet "strangely forlorn" when he was kept out of a conversation between a star and dead leaves? Why would he want to join in? What do you think they might have been talking about? Do you think the poet was inexperienced, or "innocent," to try to share their words? Is he less "innocent" at the end of the poem?

Masaccio. *Expulsion from Eden*.
Brancacci Chapel, Florence.

Georges Rouault. *Christ Mocked by Soldiers*. 1932.

Winslow Homer. *The Gulf Stream.*

189

George Tooker. *The Subway* (detail). 1950.

Autumn

The warm sun is failing, the bleak wind is wailing,
The bare boughs are sighing, the pale flowers are dying;
    And the year
On the earth her deathbed, in a shroud of leaves dead,
    Is lying.
      Come, months, come away,
      From November to May,
      In your saddest array;
      Follow the bier
      Of the dead cold year,
And like dim shadows watch by her sepulcher.

The chill rain is falling, the nipped worm is crawling,
The rivers are swelling, the thunder is knelling
    For the year;
The blithe swallows are flown, and the lizards each gone
    To his dwelling.
      Come, months, come away;
      Put on white, black, and gray;
      Let your light sisters play—
      Ye, follow the bier
      Of the dead cold year,
And make her grave green with tear on tear.

Percy Bysshe Shelley

This poem summons the months November to May to a funeral ritual.
Whose funeral?

Think back over the ways that death and destruction are described in this phase. Are there any selections that go beyond autumn, or death, or destruction, to tell of renewal?

The selections in the second phase of the First Story are also about younger people. How do the selections you have just read compare with those others?

Write a poem that expresses your feelings or ideas about a loss of innocence. If you think back over the selections in this last phase, you will see the kinds of images that tend to appear in poems on this theme. You might structure your poem by using alternating lines like this (fill in the blanks with your own words): begin one line with the words "He (or she or I) used to be like a ——" and begin your next line with "Now he (or she or I) is like a ——" Do not attempt rhyme. Make your poem as long or short as you like.

TRIUMPH AND DEFEAT

A Leaf-Treader

I have been treading on leaves all day until I am autumn-tired.
God knows all the color and form of leaves I have trodden on
and mired.
Perhaps I have put forth too much strength and been too
fierce from fear.
I have safely trodden underfoot the leaves of another year.

All summer long they were overhead, more lifted up than I.
To come to their final place in earth they had to pass me by.
All summer long I thought I heard them threatening under
their breath.
And when they came it seemed with a will to carry me with
them to death.

They spoke to the fugitive in my heart as if it were leaf to
leaf.
They tapped at my eyelids and touched my lips with an
invitation to grief.
But it was no reason I had to go because they had to go.
Now up, my knee, to keep on top of another year of snow.

Robert Frost

This lyric describes a temporary victory of the human will over autumn
and death. Why is the victory temporary? What is threatening about
the leaves? In what way does the poet himself almost surrender to the
menace of the leaves?

"Life is tragic..."

Life is tragic simply because the earth turns and the sun inexorably rises and sets, and one day, for each of us, the sun will go down for the last, last time. Perhaps the whole root of our trouble, the human trouble, is that we will sacrifice all the beauty of our lives, will imprison ourselves in totems, taboos, crosses, blood sacrifices, steeples, mosques, races, armies, flags, nations, in order to deny the fact of death, which is the only fact we have. It seems to me that one ought to rejoice in the *fact* of death—ought to decide, indeed, to *earn* one's death by confronting with passion the conundrum of life. One is responsible to life: It is the small beacon in that terrifying darkness from which we come and to which we shall return. One must negotiate this passage as nobly as possible, for the sake of those who are coming after us. But white Americans do not believe in death, and this is why the darkness of my skin so intimidates them. And this is also why the presence of the Negro in this country can bring about its destruction. It is the responsibility of free men to trust and to celebrate what is constant—birth, struggle, and death are constant, and so is love, though we may not always think so—and to apprehend the nature of change, to be able and willing to change. I speak of change not on the surface but in the depths—change in the sense of renewal. But renewal becomes impossible if one supposes things to be constant that are not—safety, for example, or money, or power. One clings then to chimeras, by which one can only be betrayed, and the entire hope—the entire possibility—of freedom disappears. And by destruction I mean precisely the abdication by Americans of any effort really to be free. The Negro can precipitate this abdication because white Americans have never, in all their long history, been able to look on him as a man like themselves. . . .

This past, the Negro's past, of rope, fire, torture, castration, infanticide, rape; death and humiliation; fear by day and night, fear as deep as the marrow of the bone; doubt that he was worthy of life, since everyone around him denied it; sorrow for his women, for his kinfolk, for his children, who needed his protection, and whom he could not protect; rage, hatred, and murder, hatred for white men so deep that it often turned against him and his own, and made all love, all trust, all joy impossible—this past, this endless struggle to achieve and reveal and confirm a human identity, human authority, yet contains, for all its horror, something very beautiful. I do not mean to be sentimental about suffering—enough is certainly as good as a feast—but people who cannot suffer can never grow up, can never discover who they are. That man who is forced each day to snatch his manhood, his identity, out of the fire of human cruelty that rages to destroy it knows, if he survives his effort, and even if he does not survive it, something about himself and human life that no school on earth—and, indeed, no church—can teach. He achieves his own authority, and that is unshakable. This is because, in order to save his life, he is forced to look beneath appearances, to take nothing for granted, to hear the meaning behind the words. If one is continually surviving the worst that life can bring, one eventually ceases to be controlled by a fear of what life can bring; whatever it brings must be borne. And at this level of experience one's bitterness begins to be palatable, and hatred becomes too heavy a sack to carry. The apprehension of life here so briefly and inadequately sketched has been the experience of generations of Negroes, and it helps to explain how they have endured and how they have been able to produce children of kindergarten age who can walk through mobs to get to school. It demands great force and great cunning continually to assault the mighty and indifferent fortress of white supremacy, as Negroes in this country have done so long. It demands great spiritual resilience not to hate the hater whose foot is on your neck, and an even greater miracle of perception and charity not to teach your child to hate. The Negro boys and girls who are facing mobs today come out of a long line of improbable aristocrats—the only genuine aristocrats this country has produced. I say "this country" because their frame of reference was totally American. They were hewing out of the mountain of white supremacy the stone of their individuality. I have great respect for that unsung army of black men and women who trudged down back lanes and entered back doors, saying "Yes, sir" and "No, ma'am" in order to acquire a new roof for the schoolhouse, new books, a new chemistry lab, more beds for the dormitories, more dormitories. They did not like saying "Yes, sir" and "No, ma'am," but the country was in no hurry to educate Negroes, these black men and women knew that the job had to be done, and they put their pride in their pockets in order to do it. It is very hard to believe that they were in any way inferior to the white men and women who opened those back doors. . . . But we must avoid the European error; we must not suppose that, because the situation, the ways, the perceptions of black people so radically differed from those of whites, they were racially superior. I am proud of these people not because of their color but because of their intelligence and their spiritual force and their beauty. The country should be proud of them, too, but, alas, not many people in this country even know of their existence. And the reason for this ignorance is that a knowledge of the role these people played—and play—in American life would reveal more about America to Americans than Americans wish to know. . . .

When I was very young, and was dealing with my buddies in those wine- and urine-stained hallways, something in me wondered, *What will happen to all that beauty?* For black people, though I am aware that some of us, black and white, do not know it yet, are very beautiful. And when I sat at Elijah's table and watched the baby, the women, and the men, and we talked about God's—or Allah's—vengeance, I wondered, when that vengeance was achieved, *What will happen to all that beauty then?* I could also see that the intransigence and ignorance of the white world might make that vengeance inevitable—a vengeance that does not really depend on, and cannot really be executed by, any person or organization, and that cannot be prevented by any police force or army: historical vengeance, a cosmic vengeance, based on the law that we recognize when we say, "Whatever goes up must come down." And here we are, at the center of the arc, trapped in the gaudiest, most valuable, and most improbable water wheel the world has ever seen. Everything now, we must assume, is in our hands; we have no right to assume otherwise. If we—and now I mean the relatively conscious whites and the relatively conscious blacks, who must, like lovers, insist on, or create, the consciousness of the others—do not falter in our duty now, we may be able, handful that we are, to end the racial nightmare, and achieve our country, and change the history of the world. If we do not now dare everything, the fulfillment of that prophecy, re-created from the Bible in song by a slave, is upon us: *God gave Noah the rainbow sign, No more water, the fire next time!*

James Baldwin

In this prose passage the tragedy described is actual and all-too-real. What is this tragedy? What natural metaphors does Baldwin use to suggest the certainty of tragedy? What is the meaning of the biblical prophecy at the end of this passage?

How does Baldwin suggest that there might be a kind of victory within the tragedy he talks of here?

The Man's Wife

This legend is told by the Yokuts Indians,
of the San Joaquin Valley in California.

The man's wife was a good woman, accomplished in all womanly skills and much beloved by her husband.

One day she died, leaving him bereft and alone, for they were childless. The man had no wish to go on living without his wife. He burned off his hair, smeared his face with mud, and when his wife was buried, refused to leave her grave or to eat or to be in any way consoled. He made a shallow hollow where he lay, his face turned to the grave, and there he stayed crying and blowing tobacco smoke from his pipe over the grave, and repeating from time to time, "I shall wait for you. When you leave, I shall go with you."

For two days and two nights he lay without food or sleep, waiting for his wife. Toward the end of the second night there was a stirring of the loose dirt over her, and she sat up. She did not see her husband, but sat for some time shaking the dirt from her hair, smoothing it with her hands, and tying it back with a narrow band of mink. She cleaned the clinging pieces of dirt from the strands of beads around her neck and over her breasts, then she stood up, straightening her skirt and apron. Clean and neat as in life she stood turning to the north, the south, and the east as if unsure of her directions. Finally she turned to the west, moving slowly away from the grave, westward, without speaking to her husband, still unaware that he was there watching her every motion, and crying.

Following her, the man tried again and again to put his arms around his wife, but he could not hold her; she slipped through his hands. He was, however, able to tie around her slim waist a rope of eagle's down, and clinging to one end of it, he walked a few steps behind her all through the night.

He could see her plainly as long as it was dark, but with daylight she became invisible. He was sure she must be lying across the trail, resting, because the eagledown rope lay there. The old men at home, he remembered, always said that the dead travel only during the dark of the sun. And he felt fairly sure his wife had not escaped him, for the path of the dead was plainly marked, and he could discern his wife's footprints upon it only as far as they had traveled. But as he sat patiently waiting for the sun to set and darkness to come again, keeping his eyes fixed on the trail ahead, he made out there the foot-prints of many, many others, and among them he was sure he recognized some which belonged to relatives and to old friends dead a long or a short time.

As day darkened to night there was a pull on the eagledown rope, and the wife, once more visible, got to her feet and recommenced her journey along the trail, her husband following after as on the night before. Again darkness gave way to light, the second day passing as had the first, the man's wife invisible to him, unmoving; the man holding to the rope as his clue, keeping his eyes on the trail ahead.

During the whole of the journey he neither slept nor took any food. He smoked his pipe from time to time, blowing the smoke toward his wife while he prayed and cried. So passed one like another, four nights and four days.

They were now close to the land of the dead, and as darkness obscured the day for the fourth time and he could again see his wife, she spoke at last. "Why do you follow me so far, my husband?" she said.

"Because I cannot live without you. Where you go, I shall go."

"But that is not possible." Her voice was gentle and familiar. "Go back to the land of the living while you still can find your way. I must go on, but from here it will be difficult and dangerous for you."

But the man answered her, "I mean to bring you away from that land. Or if I cannot, to stay there with you."

"I believe that that cannot be done," she said, and added coaxingly, "Don't you know—I am nothing now. You cannot by any means get my body back. It went from you when I died."

"Others have said that to me. Nonetheless I believe that I can because I so strongly will it," the man said.

His wife was troubled, but she said no more of his turning back. It would be useless to try to persuade him. It must come out as it would.

On and on they went, the trail ever steeper and narrower and rougher. At one place, it skirted a chasm so deep it appeared to be bottomless, and with only shallow footholds hewn in the rock for a crossing. Here she implored her husband to leave her, greatly fearing that he would slip and be hurled to his death. But, as before, he refused. Slowly, carefully, they made their way across the chasm. Not far beyond, the trail was blocked by two enormous boulders in uneasy balance, sliding apart and clashing together with such violence as to crush a person or animal who chanced to be caught between them. They were no real barrier to the man's wife, because her bones were of course left behind in her grave. She passed between them lightly and quickly, and watched with fear while her husband waited for them to slide apart. Hurling himself between them, repeating a prayer and clinging still to the eagledown rope, the man just made it to his wife's side before the rocks crashed together.

And so at last, on the evening of the sixth day, they came to the banks of the swift river which divides the land of the dead from that of the living—a river spanned only by a narrow, swaying bridge made of strands of grass rope.

The guardian of the bridge talked to them, as is his custom, learning who they were and the village from which they came, and telling them of their relatives who had already crossed over to the other side.

He did not try to dissuade the man from going, sensing his determination and his power. He did, however, warn him that even if his prayers and strength of purpose put him across the bridge, the dead would feel it an intrusion to have a living person amongst them.

He warned them that the bridge was treacherous in its erratic swaying and dipping, and that many fell from it into the river, from which there was no chance of rescue and where monstrous fish devoured them. He reminded them also that demon birds would fly up, trying to frighten them so that they would miss their footing and fall.

The man and his wife said they would go on. It was as the guardian said—demon birds flew before and around them filling the air with their loud cries and making even more hazardous the trip over the slippery, unsteady bridge. But they neither listened to them, nor looked down into the swift waters below. They kept their gaze ahead, the man clung to the rope around his wife's waist, and together they arrived on the far shore and stepped off the bridge into the land of the dead.

The chief of that land met them almost as they stepped from the bridge. To the man's wife he said, "You have come—you bring a companion with you?"

She answered him, "He is my husband. He is a living man."

The chief told her, "I will speak with him. Meanwhile, go with my messenger here. He will help you to find your relatives."

When she was gone with the messenger, the chief turned to her husband who was crying, his face distorted and mud-smeared from mourning, and he felt pity for him. He sent him to swim and clean himself; then he had his own daughters bring him food and drink. It had been many days since the man had eaten or drunk, and he accepted the food gratefully. Only after this did the chief question him, asking him how he could have reached this land never before visited by a living person. The man explained how he had come, and the chief said to him, "Tell me, why did you make this dangerous journey?"

"To recover my wife and take her back to the world with me. Or if I cannot do that, to stay here with her."

The chief knew this was a good and strong man, one who, having fasted and prayed, had learned much control and gained much power. He felt he must do for him what he could. He said, speaking carefully, "You should not have come. You are asking for something which we have no power to give you. You must know that we have here only your wife's shadow, that she has left behind in the grave her bones and her body. How can we give these things back to you? You should return to the world and content yourself until it is your time to die.

"Since you are come, and since I believe you to be a good man, you are welcome. But not for long. I must warn you that to the dead the smell of the living is offensive, and there will be a restiveness among them, a feeling of the impropriety of your being here at all. But stay for a little if you will. You will learn how it is with the dead, and that I speak truly. Do not by any means try to steal your wife away. Do not try to sleep with her."

The man sat apart from the dead, quiet, watching. As darkness crept over the land, campfires were lighted one after another until there was a circle of fires all around the open place kept for dancing, and the dead became visible to the man. He recognized his own relatives at one fire, and friends from long ago at another; in the light of still another fire, he saw his wife, surrounded by her own people. He was lonely, but he made no move to join his wife or his relatives, staying where he was and observing the seemingly happy and carefree dead, as they sat by their fires talking or playing the stick game. More and more as the night wore on, they left their fires to dance in the open space the round dance of the dead. He saw that his wife, too, talked, and played the stick game with the women, and that later she also danced. The dancing stopped only with the first dawn, and while the others went off, the man's wife turned back and came to her husband where he sat alone. Because of the daylight he could not see her, but she lay beside him, and they talked together all during the day. When night fell and he could see her, he desired her and tried to fondle her as he was accustomed to do in life, but almost at once he was overcome with sleep. When he wakened, she was gone to play in one of the games and to dance again with the dead.

Again she came to him when dawn began to break, and again she stayed with him, talking to him all day, and he had no thought of sleep. Again he tried to be as a husband to her when it was dark, again he slept, and again she was gone to join the other dead when he wakened.

After all this had happened for the third time, the chief came to the man to tell him that he could stay no longer, that the dead did not feel it to be right to allow a living person to remain among them. But, since he had grieved so deeply and gone through so much to be with his wife, the chief said that she would be allowed to return with him and to her life in the world of the living. He made only one condition: during the trip home, which would take six days and six nights, and until they were home again, the man must not touch his wife.

Joyously the man agreed. The wife, when the chief asked her if she wished to return to her home with her husband, said, "Yes." She knew that this is not how it is between the living and the dead, but she loved her husband, and she could see that he did not know how to live without her.

Together they left the land of the dead, going back across the bridge, between the moving rocks, and over the long trail, on and on until six days and five nights had come and gone and they were once more in country familiar to them. By the next day they would reach their own home.

But as darkness replaced the last of the light from the setting sun at their backs and the man could again see his wife looking quite as she had in life, he could wait no longer. He must and he would have her. She pleaded with him to wait through this one night. He could not. He took her—his love and his longing, his fasting and prayers all given to this moment.

The man's wife vanished, never to return to him.

The sun was high in the sky the next day when hunters from his own village found the man. He was dead, lying face down, arms outstretched, on the trail which leads to the west.

Retold by Theodora Kroeber

What makes this living man journey to the land of the dead? Can you think why it is suitable that the trail that leads to the *west* is the one that goes to the land of the dead? To get to the land of the dead, the man and his wife have to cross a river and take their chances with monstrous fish and demon birds. Are these images appropriate to the passage from life to death? Why?

In what way is this Indian story a quest myth? How does it differ from the two quest stories in the third phase of the First Story?

Is this a story of both triumph and defeat, or simply of defeat? How much of what the man "wills" himself to do does he succeed in doing? How is he like the "leaf-treader" in Frost's poem?

You might write a story about some heroic quest that involves failure. You could set the story in the "real" world or you might want to write a romance, in which case you will not be bound to present what seems realistic in ordinary life. A quest story usually involves three stages: the perilous journey, the crucial struggle, and the glorification of the hero (who has proved himself heroic whether he survives or not).

Abraham and Isaac

This play, which was popular in England in medieval times, is based on an account in the Bible. God has made a covenant, or contract, with a man named Abraham. As part of the covenant, God gives Abraham's aged wife, Sarah, a son. This son, Isaac, is the old couple's only child. If Abraham fulfills his part of the covenant, God promises to bless his descendants and give them the land of Canaan.

This play takes place when Isaac is a young boy. It tells how God decides to test Abraham's faith by asking him to sacrifice his son. Abraham's faith and Isaac's perfect innocence illustrate the triumphant aspect of tragic heroic action. The hero's willingness to surrender even his life, in a quest he doesn't understand, leads to a miracle of deliverance.

GOD.   Abraham, my servant, Abraham.

ABRAHAM.   Lo, Lord, all ready here I am.

GOD.

> Take Isaac, thy son by name,
> That thou lovest the best of all,
> And in sacrifice offer him to me
> Upon that hill there beside thee.
> Abraham, I will that so it be,
> For ought that may befall.

ABRAHAM.

> My Lord, to thee is mine intent
> Ever to be obedient.
> That son that thou to me hath sent,
> Offer I will to thee . . .

Thy bidding done shall be . . .
(*Here* ABRAHAM, *turning to his son* ISAAC, *saith:*)
Make thee ready, my dear darling,
For we must do a little thing.
This wood do on thy back it bring,
We may no longer abide.
A sword and fire I will take;
(*Here* ABRAHAM *taketh a sword and fire.*)
For sacrifice me behoves to make:
God's bidding will I not forsake,
But ever obedient be.
(*Here* ISAAC *speaketh to his father, and taketh a*
bundle of sticks and beareth after his father,
and saith:)

ISAAC.

Father, I am all ready
To do your bidding most meekly,
And to bear this wood full keen am I,
As you commanded me . . .
(*Here they go both to the place to do sacrifice.*)

ABRAHAM.

Now, Isaac son, go we our way
To yonder mount, if that we may.

ISAAC.

My dear father, I will try
To follow you well pleased.
(ABRAHAM, *being minded to slay his son* ISAAC,
lifts up his hands, and saith the following:)

ABRAHAM.

Oh! my heart will break in three,
To hear thy words I have pity;
As thou wilt, Lord, so must it be.
Lay down thy faggot, my own son dear.

ISAAC.

All ready, father, lo it is here.
But why make you such heavy cheer?
Are you any thing adread?

Father, if it be your will,
Where is the beast that we shall kill?

ABRAHAM.

Thereof, son, is none upon this hill,
That I see here in stead.

(ISAAC, *fearing lest his father would slay him, saith:*)

ISAAC.

Father, I am full sore afraid
To see you bear that drawn sword:
I hope for all middle earth
You will not slay your child.

(ABRAHAM *comforts his son, and saith:*)

ABRAHAM.

Dread thee not, my child, I say;
Our Lord will send of his godhead
Some manner of beast into this field,
Either tame or wild.

ISAAC.

Father, tell me ere I go,
Whether I shall be harmed or no.

ABRAHAM.

Ah! dear God! that me is woe!
Thou breaks my heart asunder . . .
Isaac, son, peace, I thee pray,
Thou breaks my heart in two.

ISAAC.

I pray you, father, hide nothing from me,
But tell me what you think.

ABRAHAM.

Ah! Isaac, Isaac, I must thee kill!

ISAAC.

Alas! father, is that your will,
Your own child for to spill
Upon this hill's brink?
If I have trespassed in any degree,
With a rod you may beat me;
Put up your sword, if your will be,
For I am but a child.

ABRAHAM.

    O, my dear son, I am sorry
    To do to thee this grievous thing!
    God's commandment do must I,
    His works are ever full mild.

ISAAC.

    Would God my mother were here with me!
    She would kneel down upon her knee,
    Praying you, father, if it may be,
    For to save my life . . .
    Is it God's will I shall be slain?

ABRAHAM.

    Yea, son, it cannot be denied;
    To his bidding I am bound,
    And ever to him pleasing.
    But that I do this doleful deed,
    My Lord will not quit me in my need . . .
    (Here ISAAC, *asking his father's blessing on his
      knees, saith:*)

ISAAC.

    Father, seeing you must needs do so,
    Let it pass lightly, and over go;
    Kneeling on my knees two,
    Your blessing on me spread . . .
    Father, I pray you hide my eyes,
    That I see not the sword so keen;
    Your stroke, father, would I not see,
    Lest I against it cry.

ABRAHAM.

    My dear son Isaac, speak no more,
    Thy words make my heart full sore.

ISAAC.

    O dear father, wherefore! wherefore!
    Seeing I must needs be dead,
    Of one thing I will you pray,
    Seeing I must die the death today,
    As few strokes you will make,
    When you smite off my head.

ABRAHAM.

> Thy meekness, child, makes me afraid;
> My song may be wail-a-way!

ISAAC.

> O dear father, do away, do away
> Your making so much moan!
> Now, truly, father, this talking
> Doth but make long tarrying,
> I pray you, come and make ending,
> And let me hence be gone.
> (*Here* ISAAC *riseth and cometh to his father,*
> *and* ABRAHAM *taketh him and bindeth and layeth*
> *him upon the altar to sacrifice him, and saith:*)

ABRAHAM.

> Come hither, my child, thou art so sweet,
> Thou must be bound both hand and feet.

ISAAC.

> Father, we must no more meet,
> By ought that I may see;
> But do with me then as you will,
> I must obey, and that is just,
> God's commandment to fulfill,
> For needs so must it be . . .
> Father, greet well my brethren young,
> And pray my mother of her blessing,
> I come no more under her wing,
> Farewell for ever and aye;
> But, father, I cry you mercy,
> For all that ever I have trespassed to thee,
> Forgiven, father, that it may be
> Until domesday.

ABRAHAM.

> My dear son, let be thy moans!
> My child, thou grieved me never once;
> Blessed be thou body and bones,
> And I forgive thee here!
> Now, my dear son, here shalt thou lie,
> Unto my work now must I hie;

I had as well my self to die,
As thou, my dear darling.

ISAAC.

Father, if you be to me kind,
About my head a kerchief bind,
And let me lightly out of your mind,
And soon that I were sped.
(*Here* ABRAHAM *doth kiss his son* ISAAC, *and
binds a kerchief about his head.*)

ABRAHAM.   Farewell, my sweet son of grace!
(*Here let* ISAAC *kneel down and speak:*)

ISAAC.

I pray you, father, turn down my face
A little, while you have space,
For I am full sore adread.

ABRAHAM.   To do this deed I am sorry!

ISAAC.

Yea, Lord, to thee I call and cry,
Of my soul thou have mercy,
Heartily I thee pray!

ABRAHAM.

Lord, I would fain work thy will,
This young innocent that lieth so still
Full loth were me him to kill,
By any manner a way . . .

ISAAC.

Ah! mercy, father, why tarry you so?
Smite off my head and let me go.
I pray rid me of my woe,
For now I take my leave.

ABRAHAM.

Ah! son! my heart will break in three,
To hear thee speak such words to me.
Jesu! on me thou have pity
That I have most in mind.

ISAAC.

Now, father, I see that I shall die:
Almighty God in majesty!

My soul I offer unto thee;
Lord, to it be kind.
(*Here let* ABRAHAM *take and bind his son* ISAAC
*upon the altar; let him make a sign as though he
would cut off his head with his sword; then let the
angel come and take the sword by the end and
stay it, saying:*)

ANGEL.　Abraham, my servant dear!

ABRAHAM.　Lo, Lord, I am all ready here!

ANGEL.

    Lay not thy sword in any manner
    On Isaac, thy dear darling;
    And do to him no harm.
    For thou dreads God, well know I,
    That of thy son has no mercy,
    To fulfill his bidding.
    And for his bidding thou dost aye,
    And sparest neither for fear nor fray,
    To do thy son to death today,
    Isaac, to thee full dear:
    Therefore, God hath sent by me, in faith,
    A lamb, that is both good and gay,
    To have him right here.

ABRAHAM.

    Ah! Lord of heaven, and king of bliss,
    Thy bidding shall be done, i-wiss!
    Sacrifice here sent me is,
    And all, Lord, through thy grace.
    A horned lamb here I see,
    Among the briars tied is he,
    To thee offered shall he be,
    Anon right in this place.
    (*Then let* ABRAHAM *take the lamb and kill him, and let* GOD
    say:)

GOD.

    Abraham, by my self I swear,
    For thou hast been obedient ever,
    And spared not thy son to tear,

To fulfill my bidding:
Thou shall be blessed, that pleased me,
Thy seed I shall so multiply,
As stars and sand so many have I,
Of thy body coming.
Of enemies thou shalt have power,
And of thy blood also in fear,
Thou hast been meek and gentle,
And do as I thee bade;
And of all nations, believe thou me,
Blessed ever more shall thou be,
Through fruit that shall come of thee,
And saved be through thy seed.

In the legend "Soldier Jack" in the First Story, the hero Jack has to face Death, just as Isaac does in this play. But how does Isaac differ from Jack?

In this drama, a lamb is substituted in the sacrifice for the innocent victim, Isaac. Is this appropriate? If so, why?

How does Abraham's "sacrifice" "save" a people?

In medieval times, when this play was acted, an expositor (one who explains) came on stage at the end of the action to tell the audience that the play was done "in example of Jesus." The audience was to understand that Abraham was like the Father in Heaven, and that Isaac was like his son, who was sacrificed to loosen the bonds that Satan had placed on men at the time of the Fall.

How is the idea that suffering holds a promise of renewal also found in Baldwin's essay? How does the North American Indian legend about the man's wife connect with the same idea—that there is a kind of victory to be found in suffering endured because of love?

Battle Hymn of the Republic

Mine eyes have seen the glory of the coming of the Lord;
He is trampling out the vintage where the grapes of wrath are
    stored;
He hath loosed the fateful lightning of His terrible swift
    sword;
      His truth is marching on.

Glory, glory, hallelujah! Glory, glory, hallelujah!
Glory, glory, hallelujah! His truth is marching on.

I have seen Him in the watch fires of a hundred circling
    camps;
They have builded Him an altar in the evening dews and
    damps;
I can read his righteous sentence by the dim and flaring
    lamps;
      His day is marching on.

Glory, glory, hallelujah! Glory, glory, hallelujah!
Glory, glory, hallelujah! His truth is marching on.

I have read a fiery gospel, writ in burnished rows of steel:
"As ye deal with my contemners, so with you my grace shall
    deal;
Let the Hero, born of woman, crush the serpent with his heel,
      Since God is marching on."

Glory, glory, hallelujah! Glory, glory, hallelujah!
Glory, glory, hallelujah! His truth is marching on.

He has sounded forth the trumpet that shall never call retreat;
He is sifting out the hearts of men before His judgment seat;

Oh, be swift, my soul, to answer Him! be jubilant, my feet!
    Our God is marching on.

Glory, glory, hallelujah! Glory, glory, hallelujah!
Glory, glory, hallelujah! His truth is marching on.

In the beauty of the lilies Christ was born across the sea,
With a glory in His bosom that transfigures you and me;
As He died to make men holy, let us die to make men free,
    While God is marching on.

Glory, glory, hallelujah! Glory, glory, hallelujah!
Glory, glory, hallelujah! His truth is marching on.

Julia Ward Howe

Though this hymn was written about the Civil War, it appears to be about another battle as well. What imagined future time does this "battle hymn" anticipate? What are the "grapes of wrath"? The singer says a serpent must be crushed. What does the serpent stand for? To what cause does this hymn summon citizens of the Republic?

How does the last verse suggest that in defeat, even in death, there can be victory?

Beowulf and the Dragon

The following passage is from a poem called *Beowulf,* which was composed sometime in the eighth or ninth century in Anglo-Saxon England. The passage here is translated from the Old English by a contemporary American poet. The hero Beowulf is now an old king who has ruled for fifty years. He has won great fame as a heroic warrior, who, in his youth, killed two vicious monsters, Grendel and Grendel's mother. Since that time, Beowulf has gained further glory as a wise and generous king of his people, the Geats (pronounced as "yachts"). Beowulf now must go to his last battle.

And Beowulf uttered his final boast:
  "I've never known fear; as a youth I fought
In endless battles. I am old, now,
But I will fight again, seek fame still,
If the dragon hiding in his tower dares
To face me."
           Then he said farewell to his followers,
Each in his turn, for the last time:
  "I'd use no sword, no weapon, if this beast
Could be killed without it, crushed to death
Like Grendel, gripped in my hands and torn
Limb from limb. But his breath will be burning
Hot, poison will pour from his tongue.
I feel no shame, with shield and sword
And armor, against this monster: when he comes to me
I mean to stand, not run from his shooting
Flames, stand till fate decides
Which of us wins. My heart is firm,
My hands calm: I need no hot

Words. Wait for me close by, my friends.
We shall see, soon, who will survive
This bloody battle, stand when the fighting
Is done. No one else could do
What I mean to, here, no man but me
Could hope to defeat this monster. No one
Could try. And this dragon's treasure, his gold
And everything hidden in that tower, will be mine
Or war will sweep me to a bitter death!"
    Then Beowulf rose, still brave, still strong,
And with his shield at his side, and a mail shirt on his breast,
Strode calmly, confidently, toward the tower, under
The rocky cliffs: no coward could have walked there!
And then he who'd endured dozens of desperate
Battles, who'd stood boldly while swords and shields
Clashed, the best of kings, saw
Huge stone arches and felt the heat
Of the dragon's breath, flooding down
Through the hidden entrance, too hot for anyone
To stand, a streaming current of fire
And smoke that blocked all passage. And the Geats'
Lord and leader, angry, lowered
His sword and roared out a battle cry,
A call so loud and clear that it reached through
The hoary rock, hung in the dragon's
Ear. The beast rose, angry,
Knowing a man had come—and then nothing
But war could have followed. Its breath came first,
A steaming cloud pouring from the stone,
Then the earth itself shook. Beowulf
Swung his shield into place, held it
In front of him, facing the entrance. The dragon
Coiled and uncoiled, its heart urging it
Into battle. Beowulf's ancient sword
Was waiting, unsheathed, his sharp and gleaming
Blade. The beast came closer; both of them
Were ready, each set on slaughter. The Geats'
Great prince stood firm, unmoving, prepared

Behind his high shield, waiting in his shining
Armor. The monster came quickly toward him,
Pouring out fire and smoke, hurrying
To its fate. Flames beat at the iron
Shield, and for a time it held, protected
Beowulf as he'd planned; then it began to melt,
And for the first time in his life that famous prince
Fought with fate against him, with glory
Denied him. He knew it, but he raised his sword
And struck at the dragon's scaly hide.
The ancient blade broke, bit into
The monster's skin, drew blood, but cracked
And failed him before it went deep enough, helped him
Less than he needed. The dragon leaped
With pain, thrashed and beat at him, spouting
Murderous flames, spreading them everywhere.
And the Geats' ring-giver did not boast of glorious
Victories in other wars: his weapon
Had failed him, deserted him, now when he needed it
Most, that excellent sword. Edgetho's
Famous son stared at death,
Unwilling to leave this world, to exchange it
For a dwelling in some distant place—a journey
Into darkness that all men must make, as death
Ends their few brief hours on earth.

 Quickly, the dragon came at him, encouraged
As Beowulf fell back; its breath flared,
And he suffered, wrapped around in swirling
Flames—a king, before, but now
A beaten warrior. None of his comrades
Came to him, helped him, his brave and noble
Followers; they ran for their lives, fled
Deep in a wood. And only one of them
Remained, stood there, miserable, remembering,
As a good man must, what kinship should mean.

 His name was Wiglaf, he was Wexstan's son
And a good soldier; his family had been Swedish,

Once. Watching Beowulf, he could see
How his king was suffering, burning. Remembering
Everything his lord and cousin had given him,
Armor and gold and the great estates
Wexstan's family enjoyed, Wiglaf's
Mind was made up; he raised his yellow
Shield and drew his sword—an ancient
Weapon that had once belonged to Onela's
Nephew, and that Wexstan had won, killing
The prince when he fled from Sweden, sought safety
With Herdred, and found death. And Wiglaf's father
Had carried the dead man's armor, and his sword,
To Onela, and the king had said nothing, only
Given him armor and sword and all,
Everything his rebel nephew had owned
And lost when he left this life. And Wexstan
Had kept those shining gifts, held them
For years, waiting for his son to use them,
Wear them as honorably and well as once
His father had done; then Wexstan died
And Wiglaf was his heir, inherited treasures
And weapons and land. He'd never worn
That armor, fought with that sword, until Beowulf
Called him to his side, led him into war.
But his soul did not melt, his sword was strong;
The dragon discovered his courage, and his weapon,
When the rush of battle brought them together.
    And Wiglaf, his heart heavy, uttered
The kind of words his comrades deserved:
    "I remember how we sat in the mead-hall, drinking
And boasting of how brave we'd be when Beowulf
Needed us, he who gave us these swords
And armor: all of us swore to repay him,
When the time came, kindness for kindness
—With our lives, if he needed them. He allowed us to join him,
Chose us from all his great army, thinking
Our boasting words had some weight, believing
Our promises, trusting our swords. He took us

For soldiers, for men. He meant to kill
This monster himself, our mighty king,
Fight this battle alone and unaided,
As in the days when his strength and daring dazzled
Men's eyes. But those days are over and gone
And now our lord must lean on younger
Arms. And we must go to him, while angry
Flames burn at his flesh, help
Our glorious king! By almighty God,
I'd rather burn myself than see
Flames swirling around my lord.
And who are we to carry home
Our shields before we've slain his enemy
And ours, to run back to our homes with Beowulf
So hard-pressed here? I swear that nothing
He ever did deserved an end
Like this, dying miserably and alone,
Butchered by this savage beast: we swore
That these swords and armor were each for us all!"
    Then he ran to his king, crying encouragement
As he dove through the dragon's deadly fumes:
    "Beloved Beowulf, remember how you boasted,
Once, that nothing in the world would ever
Destroy your fame: fight to keep it,
Now, be strong and brave, my noble
King, protecting life and fame
Together. My sword will fight at your side!"
    The dragon heard him, the man-hating monster,
And was angry; shining with surging flames
It came for him, anxious to return his visit.
Waves of fire swept at his shield
And the edge began to burn. His mail shirt
Could not help him, but before his hands dropped
The blazing wood Wiglaf jumped
Behind Beowulf's shield; his own was burned
To ashes. Then the famous old hero, remembering
Days of glory, lifted what was left
Of Nagling, his ancient sword, and swung it

With all his strength, smashed the gray
Blade into the beast's head. But then Nagling
Broke to pieces, as iron always
Had in Beowulf's hands. His arms
Were too strong, the hardest blade could not help him,
The most wonderfully worked. He carried them to war
But fate had decreed that the Geats' great king
Would be no better for any weapon.
    Then the monster charged again, vomiting
Fire, wild with pain, rushed out
Fierce and dreadful, its fear forgotten.
Watching for its chance it drove its tusks
Into Beowulf's neck; he staggered, the blood
Came flooding forth, fell like rain.

    And then when Beowulf needed him most
Wiglaf showed his courage, his strength
And skill, and the boldness he was born with. Ignoring
The dragon's head, he helped his lord
By striking lower down. The sword
Sank in; his hand was burned, but the shining
Blade had done its work, the dragon's
Belching flames began to flicker
And die away. And Beowulf drew
His battle-sharp dagger: the blood-stained old king
Still knew what he was doing. Quickly, he cut
The beast in half, slit it apart.
It fell, their courage had killed it, two noble
Cousins had joined in the dragon's death.
Yet what they did all men must do
When the time comes! But the triumph was the last
Beowulf would ever earn, the end
Of greatness and life together. The wound
In his neck began to swell and grow;
He could feel something stirring, burning
In his veins, a stinging venom, and knew
The beast's fangs had left it. He fumbled
Along the wall, found a slab

Of stone, and dropped down; above him he saw
Huge stone arches and heavy posts,
Holding up the roof of that giant hall.
Then Wiglaf's gentle hands bathed
The blood-stained prince, his glorious lord,
Weary of war, and loosened his helmet.

    Beowulf spoke, in spite of the swollen,
Livid wound, knowing he'd unwound
His string of days on earth, seen
As much as God would grant him; all worldly
Pleasure was gone, as life would go,
Soon:

        "I'd leave my armor to my son,
Now, if God had given me an heir,
A child born of my body, his life
Created from mine. I've worn this crown
For fifty winters: no neighboring people
Have tried to threaten the Geats, sent soldiers
Against us or talked of terror. My days
Have gone by as fate willed, waiting
For its word to be spoken, ruling as well
As I knew how, swearing no unholy oaths,
Seeking no lying wars. I can leave
This life happy; I can die, here,
Knowing the Lord of all life has never
Watched me wash my sword in blood
Born of my own family. Beloved
Wiglaf, go, quickly, find
The dragon's treasure: we've taken its life,
But its gold is ours, too. Hurry,
Bring me ancient silver, precious
Jewels, shining armor and gems,
Before I die. Death will be softer,
Leaving life and this people I've ruled
So long, if I look at this last of all prizes."

    Then Wexstan's son went in, as quickly
As he could, did as the dying Beowulf

Asked, entered the inner darkness
Of the tower, went with his mail shirt and his sword.
Flushed with victory he groped his way,
A brave young warrior, and suddenly saw
Piles of gleaming gold, precious
Gems, scattered on the floor, cups
And bracelets, rusty old helmets, beautifully
Made but rotting with no hands to rub
And polish them. They lay where the dragon left them;
It had flown in the darkness, once, before fighting
Its final battle. (So gold can easily
Triumph, defeat the strongest of men,
No matter how deep it is hidden!) And he saw,
Hanging high above, a golden
Banner, woven by the best of weavers
And beautiful. And over everything he saw
A strange light, shining everywhere,
On walls and floor and treasure. Nothing
Moved, no other monsters appeared;
He took what he wanted, all the treasures
That pleased his eye, heavy plates
And golden cups and the glorious banner,
Loaded his arms with all they could hold.
Beowulf's dagger, his iron blade,
Had finished the fire-spitting terror
That once protected tower and treasures
Alike; the gray-bearded lord of the Geats
Had ended those flying, burning raids
Forever.
       Then Wiglaf went back, anxious
To return while Beowulf was alive, to bring him
Treasure they'd won together. He ran,
Hoping his wounded king, weak
And dying, had not left the world too soon.
Then he brought their treasure to Beowulf, and found
His famous king bloody, gasping
For breath. But Wiglaf sprinkled water
Over his lord, until the words

Deep in his breast broke through and were heard.
Beholding the treasure he spoke, haltingly:
    "For this, this gold, these jewels, I thank
Our Father in Heaven, Ruler of the Earth—
For all of this, that his grace has given me,
Allowed me to bring to my people while breath
Still came to my lips. I sold my life
For this treasure, and I sold it well. Take
What I leave, Wiglaf, lead my people,
Help them; my time is gone. Have
The brave Geats build me a tomb,
When the funeral flames have burned me, and build it
Here, at the water's edge, high
On this spit of land, so sailors can see
This tower, and remember my name, and call it
Beowulf's tower, and boats in the darkness
And mist, crossing the sea, will know it."
    Then that brave king gave the golden
Necklace from around his throat to Wiglaf,
Gave him his gold-covered helmet, and his rings,
And his mail shirt, and ordered him to use them well:
    "You're the last of all our far-flung family.
Fate has swept our race away,
Taken warriors in their strength and led them
To the death that was waiting. And now I follow them."
    The old man's mouth was silent, spoke
No more, had said as much as it could;
He would sleep in the fire, soon. His soul
Left his flesh, flew to glory.

Translated by Burton Raffel

What reasons are given for Beowulf's willingness to fight the dragon?

What kind of hero is he? Is he in any way like Abraham? Is this type of hero described anywhere in "The Battle Hymn of the Republic"?

Is Beowulf's last great adventure more a victory or a defeat? Why?

What do you think is the meaning of the dragon in this story? How is the dragon like, or unlike, the other monsters you have read about so far in this book? Could you say that in tragedy the "dragon" is often Death?

Reread Tolkien's poem "The Hoard" in the First Story. Do you see any important connections between it and this passage from *Beowulf?*

In one part of this story, we read that Beowulf "stared at death,/Unwilling to leave this world, to exchange it/For a dwelling in some distant place—a journey/Into darkness that all men must make...." Find the passages in James Baldwin's essay that connect with these words.

Think back over the six selections in this group—a modern lyric, a nonfictional prose piece, an Indian myth, a medieval play, a hymn, and part of an Old English epic poem. Can you see how they all deal with the theme that victory is sometimes to be found within tragedy?

Which characters thus far in the Second Story begin as innocent of evil, but end up "knowing" or "experienced"?

PRIDE AND DEATH

John Henry

Moderate blues tempo

John Hen-ry was a ___ lit-tle ba-by boy, ___ You could hold him in the palm of your hand, ___ He ___ gave a long ___ and a lone-some cry, "Gon-na be a steel-driv - in' man, Lawd, Lawd, Gon-na be a steel-driv - in' man."

2 / They took John Henry to the tunnel,
Put him in the lead to drive,
The rock was so tall, John Henry so small,
That he lied down his hammer and he cried, Lawd, Lawd,
Lied down his hammer and he cried.

3 / John Henry started on the right hand,
The steam drill started on the left,
"Fo' I'd let that steamdrill beat me down,
I'd hammer my fool self to death, Lawd, Lawd,
I'd hammer my fool self to death."

4 / John Henry told his captain,
"A man ain't nothin' but a man,
Fo' I let your steamdrill beat me down
I'll die with this hammer in my hand, Lawd, Lawd,
I'll die with this hammer in my hand."

5 / John Henry had a little woman
Her name were Polly Anne,
John Henry took sick and he had to go to bed,
Polly Anne drove steel like a man, Lawd, Lawd,
Polly Anne drove steel like a man.

6 / Now the Captain told John Henry,
"I b'lieve my tunnel's sinkin' in."
"Stand back, Captain, and doncha be afraid,
That's nothin' but my hammer catchin' wind, Lawd, Lawd,
That's nothin' but my hammer catchin' wind."

7 / John Henry he told his shaker,
"Now shaker, why don't you sing?
I'm throwin' nine pounds from my hips on down,
Just listen to the cold steel ring, Lawd, Lawd,
Just listen to the cold steel ring."

8 / John Henry he told his shaker,
"Now shaker, why don't you pray?
For if I miss this six-foot steel
Tomorrow'll be your buryin' day, Lawd, Lawd,
Tomorrow'll be your buryin' day."

9 / John Henry he told his Captain,
   "Looky yonder, boy, what do I see?
   Your drill's done broke and your hole's done choke,
   And you can't drive steel like me, Lawd, Lawd,
   And you can't drive steel like me."

10 / John Henry hammerin' in the mountain
   Till the handle of his hammer caught on fire,
   He drove so hard till he broke his poor heart,
   Then he lied down his hammer and he died, Lawd, Lawd,
   Then he lied down his hammer and he died.

11 / Women in the west heard of John Henry's death
   They couldn't hardly stay in bed,
   Stood in the rain, flagged that east-bound train
   "Goin' where that man fell dead, Lawd, Lawd,
   Goin' where that man fell dead."

12 / They took John Henry to the tunnel,
   And they buried him in the sand,
   An' every locomotive come rollin' by
   Say, "There lays a steel-drivin' man, Lawd, Lawd,
   There lays a steel-drivin' man."

13 / Now some say he come from England,
   And some say he come from Spain,
   But I say he's nothin' but a Lou'siana man,
   Leader of a steel-drivin' gang, Lawd, Lawd,
   Leader of a steel-drivin' gang.

How can John Henry's death be seen as the result of reckless pride?

How is John Henry's story like Beowulf's? In what crucial way is it different?

Death

Nor dread nor hope attend
A dying animal;
A man awaits his end
Dreading and hoping all;
Many times he died,
Many times rose again,
A great man in his pride
Confronting murderous men
Casts derision upon
Supersession of breath;
He knows death to the bone—
Man has created death.

William Butler Yeats

How does man's dying differ from that of an animal, according to this poem? Yeats says that a great, proud man mocks or derides death (which he calls the "supersession of breath") because such a man "knows death to the bone." What does he mean? How has man "created" death?

Does the idea that man has "created" death refer to the story of the Fall of man described in the passage from Genesis in this Second Story? How does James Baldwin regard death, according to his essay earlier in this book?

"How art thou fallen from heaven,

O Lucifer..."

How art thou fallen from heaven, O Lucifer, son of the morning! How art thou cut down to the ground, which didst weaken the nations!

For thou hast said in thine heart, "I will ascend into heaven, I will exalt my throne above the stars of God. I will sit also upon the mount of the congregation, in the sides of the north:

"I will ascend above the heights of the clouds; I will be like the Most High."

Yet thou shalt be brought down to hell, to the sides of the pit.

They that see thee shall narrowly look upon thee, and consider thee, saying, "Is this the man that made the earth to tremble, that did shake kingdoms;

"That made the world as a wilderness, and destroyed the cities thereof; that opened not the house of his prisoners?"

All the kings of the nations, even all of them, lie in glory, every one in his own house.

But thou art cast out of thy grave like an abominable branch, and as the raiment of those that are slain, thrust through with a sword, that go down to the stones of the pit; as a carcass trodden under feet.

Isaiah 14, 12–19

What did Lucifer try to do in heaven that caused his fall? What images of height and of depth show the vastness of Lucifer's fall?

(page opposite) Albrecht Dürer. *The Knight, Death and the Devil.*

Vision of Belshazzar

This poem is based on an episode in the Bible. The incident takes place in the court of Belshazzar, King of the Chaldeans. The Chaldeans plundered the temple at Jerusalem and were holding the Jews in captivity in the city of Babel. The young captive in this story who can interpret the handwriting on the wall is the prophet Daniel.

The King was on his throne,
    The satraps thronged the hall;
A thousand bright lamps shone
    O'er that high festival.
A thousand cups of gold,
    In Judah deemed divine—
Jehovah's vessels hold
    The godless heathen's wine!

In that same hour and hall,
    The fingers of a hand
Came forth against the wall,
    And wrote as if on sand;
The fingers of a man—
    A solitary hand
Along the letters ran,
    And traced them like a wand.

The monarch saw, and shook,
    And bade no more rejoice;
All bloodless waxed his look,
    And tremulous his voice.
"Let the men of lore appear,
    The wisest of the earth,
And expound the words of fear
    Which mar our royal mirth."

Chaldea's seers are good,
    But here they have no skill;
And the unknown letters stood
    Untold and awful still.

And Babel's men of age
    Are wise and deep in lore;
But now they were not sage,
    They saw—but knew no more.

A captive in the land,
    A stranger and a youth,
He heard the king's command,
    He saw that writing's truth.
The lamps around were bright,
    The prophecy in view;
He read it on that night—
    The morrow proved it true.

"Belshazzar's grave is made,
    His kingdom passed away,
He, in the balance weighed,
    Is light and worthless clay.
The shroud, his robe of state,
    His canopy the stone;
The Mede is at his gate!
    The Persian on his throne!"

George Gordon, Lord Byron

What details of the prophecy illustrate the fleeting nature of Belshazzar's proud achievements as king? How soon is the prophecy shown to be true?

Is the description of Belshazzar's tragedy in any way like the description of Lucifer's?

The Castle

All through that summer at ease we lay,
And daily from the turret wall
We watched the mowers in the hay
And the enemy half a mile away.
They seemed no threat to us at all.

For what, we thought, had we to fear
With our arms and provender, load on load,
Our towering battlements, tier on tier,
And friendly allies drawing near
On every leafy summer road.

Our gates were strong, our walls were thick,
So smooth and high, no man could win
A foothold there, no clever trick
Could take us, have us dead or quick.
Only a bird could have got in.

What could they offer us for bait?
Our captain was brave and we were true . . .
There was a little private gate,
A little wicked wicket gate.
The wizened warder let them through.

Oh then our maze of tunnelled stone
Grew thin and treacherous as air.
The cause was lost without a groan,
The famous citadel overthrown,
And all its secret galleries bare.

How can this shameful tale be told?
I will maintain until my death
We could do nothing, being sold;
Our only enemy was gold,
And we had no arms to fight it with.

Edwin Muir

What details in this poem tell you that those in the castle felt a sense of security? How is the catastrophe caused by that sense of security being misplaced? What other factor brings about the defeat of those in the castle?

At this point in the Second Story, we have moved into a world in which innocence itself has died. Innocent heroes have disappeared from this world, and the people in it are more and more ordinary, more like ourselves. They are fully aware that they must die, that they cannot live forever. They are the victims of terrible suffering or bitter experience. At times, they are capable of great cruelty against others and against themselves. A world in which man knows that he can "give" death to other people is no longer an innocent world. We are now in the world of experience.

NOTHINGNESS

The Listeners

"Is there anybody there?" said the Traveller,
    Knocking on the moonlit door;
And his horse in the silence champed the grasses
    Of the forest's ferny floor:
And a bird flew up out of the turret,
    Above the Traveller's head:
And he smote upon the door again a second time;
    "Is there anybody there?" he said.
But no one descended to the Traveller;
    No head from the leaf-fringed sill
Leaned over and looked into his gray eyes,
    Where he stood perplexed and still.
But only a host of phantom listeners
    That dwelt in the lone house then
Stood listening in the quiet of the moonlight
    To that voice from the world of men:
Stood thronging the faint moonbeams on the dark stair,
    That goes down to the empty hall,
Hearkening in an air stirred and shaken
    By the lonely Traveller's call.
And he felt in his heart their strangeness,
    Their stillness answering his cry,
While his horse moved, cropping the dark turf,
    'Neath the starred and leafy sky;

For he suddenly smote on the door, even
    Louder, and lifted his head:—
"Tell them I came, and no one answered,
    That I kept my word," he said.
Never the least stir made the listeners,
    Though every word he spake
Fell echoing through the shadowiness of the still house
    From the one man left awake:
Ay, they heard his foot upon the stirrup,
    And the sound of iron on stone,
And how the silence surged softly backward,
    When the plunging hoofs were gone.

Walter de la Mare

This poem describes an experience of the supernatural. A human voice speaks but receives no answer, although silent phantoms listen intently. Do you think this poem expresses the theme of wasted human effort? Why?

The Quest for Leza

This legend is told by the Baila people of Africa.

She was an old woman of a family with a long genealogy. Leza Shi-kakunamo—"The Besetting One"—had stretched out his hand against her family. He slew her mother and her father while she was yet a child; and in the course of the years all connected with her perished. She said to herself, "Surely, I shall keep those who sit on my thighs"—but no, even they, the children of her children, were taken from her. She became withered with age, and it seemed to her that she herself was at last to be taken. But no, a change came over her: she grew younger. Then came into her heart a desperate resolution to find God and ask the meaning of it all. Somewhere up there in the sky must be his dwelling: if only she could reach it!

She began to cut down trees, immense, tall trees, joining them together, and so planning a structure that would reach to heaven. It grew and grew, but as it was getting to be as she wanted it, the lowest timbers rotted and it fell. She fell with it, but without being killed or breaking a bone. She set to work again and rebuilt the structure, but once again the foundations rotted and it fell. She gave it up in despair, but not her intention of finding Leza. Somewhere on earth there must be another way to heaven!

So she began to travel, going through country after country, nation after nation, always with the thought in her mind: "I shall come to where the earth ends, and there, where the earth and sky touch, I shall find a road to God, and I shall ask him, 'What have I done to thee that thou afflictest me in this manner?'"

The old woman never found where the earth ends, but, though disappointed, she did not give up her search. As she passed through the different countries, the people asked her, "What have you come for, old woman?"

And her answer would be, "I am seeking Leza."

"Seeking Leza! For what?"

"My brothers, you ask me! Here in the nations is there one who suffers as I have suffered?"

And they would ask again, "How have you suffered?"

"In this way. I am alone. As you see me, a solitary old woman: that is how I am!"

And they answered again, "Yes, we see. That is how you are! Bereaved of friends and kindred? In what do you differ from others? Leza Shikakunamo sits on the back of every one of us, and we cannot shake him off!"

She never obtained her desire: she died of a broken heart.

What does Leza represent?

"Somewhere up there in the sky must be his dwelling: if only she could reach it!" What does the old woman do to try to fulfill her wish? What happens?

If this legend were placed with the romance literature of our First Story, how would it have to end?

Is this old woman even more "experienced" with suffering than John Henry is? Is she as heroic a figure as he is? Why?

"Where does one
run to...?"

I want to talk about the first Northern urban generation of Negroes. I want to talk about the experiences of a misplaced generation, of a misplaced people in an extremely complex, confused society. This is a story of their searching, their dreams, their sorrows, their small and futile rebellions, and their endless battle to establish their own place in America's greatest metropolis—and in America itself.

The characters are sons and daughters of former Southern sharecroppers. These were the poorest people of the South, who poured into New York City during the decade following the Great Depression. These migrants were told that unlimited opportunities for prosperity existed in New York and that there was no "color problem" there. They were told that Negroes lived in houses with bathrooms, electricity, running water, and indoor toilets. To them, this was the "promised land" that Mammy had been singing about in the cotton fields for many years.

Going to New York was good-by to the cotton fields, good-by to "Massa Charlie," good-by to the chain gang, and, most of all, good-by to those sunup-to-sundown working hours. One no longer had to wait to get to heaven to lay his burden down; burdens could be laid down in New York.

So, they came, from all parts of the South, like all the black chillun o' God following the sound of Gabriel's horn on that long-overdue Judgment Day. The Georgians came as soon as they were able to pick train fare off the peach trees. They came from South Carolina where the cotton stalks were bare. The North Carolinians came with tobacco tar beneath their fingernails.

They felt as the Pilgrims must have felt when they were coming to America. But these descendants of Ham must have been twice as happy as the Pilgrims, because they had been catching twice the hell. Even while planning the trip, they sang spirituals as "Jesus Take My Hand" and "I'm On My Way" and chanted, "Hallelujah, I'm on my way to the promised land!"

It seems that Cousin Willie, in his lying haste, had neglected to tell the folks down home about one of the most important aspects of the promised land: it was a slum ghetto. There was a tremendous difference in the way life was lived up North. There were too many people full of hate and bitterness crowded into a dirty, stinky, uncared-for closet-size section of a great city.

Before the soreness of the cotton fields had left Mama's back, her knees were getting sore from scrubbing floors. Nevertheless, she was better off; she had gone from the fire into the frying pan.

The children of these disillusioned colored pioneers inherited the total lot of their parents—the disappointments, the anger. To add to their misery, they had little hope of deliverance. For where does one run to when he's already in the promised land?

Claude Brown

What kind of life did the southern blacks escape to when they went to New York? What did they think they were going to? What was the result? How does Brown put the black people in a biblical situation? Why can you say that he is writing about a "failed quest"? What is the realization reached at the end of the passage? Compare the quest of these followers of Gabriel's horn with the quest of the old woman for Leza.

In the Evenin', Mama

Well, if I could holler just like a mountain Jack,
Then I would go 'way up on a mountaintop,
And I would call, and I would call,
And I would call my baby back.
Ooh . . . in the evenin',
It's so hard, it's so hard, I declare, in the evenin',
When the sun go down.
In the evenin', in the evenin', Mama,
Mama, when the sun go down,
In the evenin', in the evenin', pretty Mama,
When the sun go down,
Don't you feel mighty lonesome,
Yes, I declare, in the evenin', when the sun go down,
When the sun go down.

Riders to the Sea

J. M. Synge

In certain remote Irish fishing villages, women knit
sweaters with unique patterns for their husbands, sons,
and brothers. The seas are wild around the Irish coasts,
and many of the men are eventually drowned. When
their decomposed bodies are washed ashore, it is often
the sweaters that help the women identify the victims,
and so be able to give their men proper burial.

Characters

MAURYA, *an old woman*   NORA, *a younger daughter*
BARTLEY, *her son*   MEN *and* WOMEN
CATHLEEN, *her daughter*

Scene: An island off the west of Ireland.

*Cottage kitchen, with net, oilskins, spinning wheel, some new boards
standing by the wall, etc.* CATHLEEN, *a girl of about twenty, finishes
kneading cake, and puts it down in the pot-oven by the fire; then
wipes her hands, and begins to spin at the wheel.* NORA, *a young girl,
puts her head in at the door.*

NORA (*in a low voice*).   Where is she?

CATHLEEN.   She's lying down, God help her, and may be sleeping, if she's
able.

(NORA *comes in softly, and takes a bundle from under her shawl.*)

CATHLEEN (*spinning the wheel rapidly*).   What is it you have?

NORA.   The young priest is after bringing them. It's a shirt and a plain stocking were got off a drowned man in Donegal.

(CATHLEEN *stops her wheel with a sudden movement, and leans out to listen.*)

NORA.   We're to find out if it's Michael's they are, some time herself will be down looking by the sea.

CATHLEEN.   How would they be Michael's, Nora? How would he go the length of that way to the far north?

NORA.   The young priest says he's known the like of it. "If it's Michael's they are," says he, "you can tell herself he's got a clean burial by the grace of God, and if they're not his, let no one say a word about them, for she'll be getting her death," says he, "with crying and lamenting."

(*The door which* NORA *half-closed is blown open by a gust of wind.*)

CATHLEEN (*looking out anxiously*).   Did you ask him would he stop Bartley going this day with the horses to the Galway fair?

NORA.   "I won't stop him," says he, "but let you not be afraid. Herself does be saying prayers half through the night, and the Almighty God won't leave her destitute," says he, "with no son living."

CATHLEEN.   Is the sea bad by the white rocks, Nora?

NORA.   Middling bad, God help us. There's a great roaring in the west, and it's worse it'll be getting when the tide's turned to the wind. (*She goes over to the table with the bundle.*) Shall I open it now?

CATHLEEN.   Maybe she'd wake up on us, and come in before we'd done. (*Coming to the table*) It's a long time we'll be, and the two of us crying.

NORA (*goes to the inner door and listens*).   She's moving about on the bed. She'll be coming in a minute.

CATHLEEN.   Give me the ladder, and I'll put them up in the turf-loft, that way she won't know of them at all, and maybe when the tide turns she'll be going down to see would he be floating from the east.

(*They put the ladder against the gable of the chimney;* CATHLEEN *goes up a few steps and hides the bundle in the turf-loft.* MAURYA *comes from the inner room.*)

MAURYA (*looking up at* CATHLEEN *and speaking querulously*). Isn't it turf enough you have for this day and evening?

CATHLEEN. There's a cake baking at the fire for a short space (*throwing down the turf*) and Bartley will want it when the tide turns if he goes to Connemara. (NORA *picks up the turf and puts it round the pot-oven.*)

MAURYA (*sitting down on a stool at the fire*). He won't go this day with the wind rising from the south and west. He won't go this day, for the young priest will stop him surely.

NORA. He'll not stop him, Mother, and I heard Eamon Simon and Stephen Pheety and Colum Shawn saying he would go.

MAURYA. Where is he itself?

NORA. He went down to see would there be another boat sailing in the week, and I'm thinking it won't be long till he's here now, for the tide's turning at the green head, and the hooker's tacking from the east.

CATHLEEN. I hear someone passing the big stones.

NORA (*looking out*). He's coming now, and he in a hurry.

BARTLEY (*comes in and looks round the room. Speaking sadly and quietly*). Where is the bit of new rope, Cathleen, was bought in Connemara?

CATHLEEN (*coming down*). Give it to him, Nora; it's on a nail by the white boards. I hung it up this morning, for the pig with the black feet was eating it.

NORA (*giving him a rope*). Is that it, Bartley?

MAURYA. You'd do right to leave that rope, Bartley, hanging by the boards. (BARTLEY *takes the rope.*) It will be wanting in this place, I'm telling you, if Michael is washed up tomorrow morning, or the next morning, or any morning in the week, for it's a deep grave we'll make him by the grace of God.

BARTLEY (*beginning to work with the rope*). I've no halter the way I can ride down on the mare, and I must go now quickly. This is the one boat going for two weeks or beyond it, and the fair will be a good fair for horses I heard them saying below.

MAURYA. It's a hard thing they'll be saying below if the body is washed up and there's no man in it to make the coffin, and I after giving a big price for the finest white boards you'd find in Connemara. (*She looks round at the boards.*)

BARTLEY. How would it be washed up, and we after looking each day for nine days, and a strong wind blowing a while back from the west and south?

MAURYA. If it wasn't found itself, that wind is raising the sea, and there was a star up against the moon, and it rising in the night. If it was a hundred horses, or a thousand horses you had itself, what is the price of a thousand horses against a son where there is one son only?

BARTLEY (*working at the halter, to* CATHLEEN). Let you go down each day, and see the sheep aren't jumping in on the rye, and if the jobber comes you can sell the pig with the black feet if there is a good price going.

MAURYA. How would the like of her get a good price for a pig?

BARTLEY (*to* CATHLEEN). If the west wind holds with the last bit of the moon let you and Nora get up weed enough for another cock for the kelp. It's hard set we'll be from this day with no one in it but one man to work.

MAURYA. It's hard set we'll be surely the day you're drownd'd with the rest. What way will I live and the girls with me, and I an old woman looking for the grave? (BARTLEY *lays down the halter, takes off his old coat, and puts on a newer one of the same flannel.*)

BARTLEY (*to* NORA). Is she coming to the pier?

NORA (*looking out*). She's passing the green head and letting fall her sails.

BARTLEY (*getting his purse and tobacco*). I'll have half an hour to go down, and you'll see me coming again in two days, or in three days, or maybe in four days if the wind is bad.

MAURYA (*turning round to the fire, and putting her shawl over her head*). Isn't it a hard and cruel man won't hear a word from an old woman, and she holding him from the sea?

CATHLEEN. It's the life of a young man to be going on the sea, and who would listen to an old woman with one thing and she saying it over?

BARTLEY (*taking the halter*). I must go now quickly. I'll ride down on the red mare, and the gray pony'll run behind me. . . . The blessing of God on you. (*He goes out.*)

MAURYA (*crying out as he is in the door*). He's gone now, God spare us, and we'll not see him again. He's gone now, and when the black night is falling I'll have no son left me in the world.

CATHLEEN. Why wouldn't you give him your blessing and he looking round in the door? Isn't it sorrow enough is on everyone in this house without your sending him out with an unlucky word behind him, and a hard word in his ear? (MAURYA *takes up the tongs and begins raking the fire aimlessly without looking round.*)

NORA (*turning toward her*).   You're taking away the turf from the cake.

CATHLEEN (*crying out*).   The Son of God forgive us, Nora, we're after forgetting his bit of bread. (*She comes over to the fire.*)

NORA.   And it's destroyed he'll be going till dark night, and he after eating nothing since the sun went up.

CATHLEEN (*turning the cake out of the oven*).   It's destroyed he'll be, surely. There's no sense left on any person in a house where an old woman will be talking for ever.

(MAURYA *sways herself on her stool.*)

CATHLEEN (*cutting off some of the bread and rolling it in a cloth; to* MAURYA).   Let you go down now to the spring well and give him this and he passing. You'll see him then and the dark world will be broken, and you can say "God speed you," the way he'll be easy in his mind.

MAURYA (*taking the bread*).   Will I be in it as soon as himself?

CATHLEEN.   If you go now quickly.

MAURYA (*standing up unsteadily*).   It's hard set I am to walk.

CATHLEEN (*looking at her anxiously*).   Give her the stick, Nora, or maybe she'll slip on the big stones.

NORA.   What stick?

CATHLEEN.   The stick Michael brought from Connemara.

MAURYA (*taking a stick* NORA *gives her*).   In the big world the old people do be leaving things after them for their sons and children, but in this place it is the young men do be leaving things behind for them that do be old. (*She goes out slowly.* NORA *goes over to the ladder.*)

CATHLEEN.   Wait, Nora, maybe she'd turn back quickly. She's that sorry, God help her, you wouldn't know the thing she'd do.

NORA.   Is she gone round by the bush?

CATHLEEN (*looking out*).   She's gone now. Throw it down quickly, for the Lord knows when she'll be out of it again.

NORA (*getting the bundle from the loft*).   The young priest said he'd be passing tomorrow, and we might go down and speak to him below if it's Michael's they are surely.

CATHLEEN (*taking the bundle*).   Did he say what way they were found?

NORA (*coming down*).   "There were two men," says he, "and they rowing round with poteen [1] before the cocks crowed, and the oar of one of them caught the body, and they passing the black cliffs of the north."

CATHLEEN (*trying to open the bundle*).   Give me a knife, Nora, the string's perished with the salt water, and there's a black knot on it you wouldn't loosen in a week.

NORA (*giving her a knife*).   I've heard tell it was a long way to Donegal.

CATHLEEN (*cutting the string*).   It is surely. There was a man in here a while ago—the man sold us that knife—and he said if you set off walking from the rocks beyond, it would be seven days you'd be in Donegal.

NORA.   And what time would a man take, and he floating?

(CATHLEEN *opens the bundle and takes out a bit of a stocking. They look at them eagerly.*)

CATHLEEN (*in a low voice*).   The Lord spare us, Nora! isn't it a queer hard thing to say if it's his they are surely?

NORA.   I'll get his shirt off the hook the way we can put the one flannel on the other. (*She looks through some clothes hanging in the corner.*) It's not with them, Cathleen, and where will it be?

CATHLEEN.   I'm thinking Bartley put it on him in the morning, for his own shirt was heavy with the salt in it. (*Pointing to the corner*) There's a bit of a sleeve was of the same stuff. Give me that and it will do.

(NORA *brings it to her and they compare the flannel.*)

CATHLEEN.   It's the same stuff, Nora; but if it is itself aren't there great rolls of it in the shops of Galway, and isn't it many another man may have a shirt of it as well as Michael himself?

NORA (*who has taken up the stocking and counted the stitches, crying out*).   It's Michael, Cathleen, it's Michael; God spare his soul, and what will herself say when she hears this story, and Bartley on the sea?

CATHLEEN (*taking the stocking*).   It's a plain stocking.

NORA.   It's the second one of the third pair I knitted, and I put up three

---

[1] **poteen** (po·cheen′): homemade whiskey.

score stitches, and I dropped four of them.

CATHLEEN (*counts the stitches*). It's that number is in it. (*Crying out*) Ah, Nora, isn't it a bitter thing to think of him floating that way to the far north, and no one to keen him but the black hags that do be flying on the sea?

NORA (*swinging herself round, and throwing out her arms on the clothes*). And isn't it a pitiful thing when there is nothing left of a man who was a great rower and fisher, but a bit of an old shirt and a plain stocking?

CATHLEEN (*after an instant*). Tell me is herself coming, Nora? I hear a little sound on the path.

NORA (*looking out*). She is, Cathleen. She's coming up to the door.

CATHLEEN. Put these things away before she'll come in. Maybe it's easier she'll be after giving her blessing to Bartley, and we won't let on we've heard anything the time he's on the sea.

NORA (*helping* CATHLEEN *to close the bundle*). We'll put them here in the corner. (*They put them into a hole in the chimney corner.* CATHLEEN *goes back to the spinning-wheel.*)

NORA. Will she see it was crying I was?

CATHLEEN. Keep your back to the door the way the light'll not be on you.

(NORA *sits down at the chimney corner, with her back to the door.* MAURYA *comes in very slowly, without looking at the girls, and goes over to her stool at the other side of the fire. The cloth with the bread is still in her hand. The girls look at each other, and* NORA *points to the bundle of bread.*)

CATHLEEN (*after spinning for a moment*). You didn't give him his bit of bread?

(MAURYA *begins to keen softly, without turning round.*)

CATHLEEN. Did you see him riding down?

(MAURYA *goes on keening.*)

CATHLEEN (*a little impatiently*). God forgive you; isn't it a better thing to raise your voice and tell what you seen, than to be making lamentation for a thing that's done? Did you see Bartley, I'm saying to you.

MAURYA (*with a weak voice*). My heart's broken from this day.

CATHLEEN (*as before*).   Did you see Bartley?

MAURYA.   I seen the fearfulest thing.

CATHLEEN (*leaves her wheel and looks out*).   God forgive you; he's riding the mare now over the green head, and the gray pony behind him.

MAURYA (*starts, so that her shawl falls back from her head and shows her white tossed hair. With a frightened voice*).   The gray pony behind him.

CATHLEEN (*coming to the fire*).   What is it ails you, at all?

MAURYA (*speaking very slowly*).   I've seen the fearfulest thing any person has seen, since the day Bride Dara seen the dead man with the child in his arms.

CATHLEEN *and* NORA.   Uah. (*They crouch down in front of the old woman at the fire.*)

NORA.   Tell us what it is you seen.

MAURYA.   I went down to the spring well, and I stood there saying a prayer to myself. Then Bartley came along, and he riding on the red mare with the gray pony behind him. (*She puts up her hands, as if to hide something from her eyes.*) The Son of God spare us, Nora!

CATHLEEN.   What is it you seen?

MAURYA.   I seen Michael himself.

CATHLEEN (*speaking softly*).   You did not, Mother; it wasn't Michael you seen, for his body is after being found in the far north, and he's got a clean burial by the grace of God.

MAURYA (*a little defiantly*).   I'm after seeing him this day, and he riding and galloping. Bartley came first on the red mare; and I tried to say "God speed you," but something choked the words in my throat. He went by quickly; and "the blessing of God on you," says he, and I could say nothing. I looked up then, and I crying, at the gray pony, and there was Michael upon it—with fine clothes on him, and new shoes on his feet.

CATHLEEN (*begins to keen*).   It's destroyed we are from this day. It's destroyed, surely.

NORA.   Didn't the young priest say the Almighty God wouldn't leave her destitute with no son living?

MAURYA (*in a low voice, but clearly*).   It's little the like of him knows of the sea. . . . Bartley will be lost now, and let you call in Eamon and make me a good coffin out of the white boards, for I won't live after them. I've had a husband, and a husband's father, and six sons in this

house—six fine men, though it was a hard birth I had with every one of them and they coming to the world—and some of them were found and some of them were not found, but they're gone now the lot of them. . . . There were Stephen, and Shawn, were lost in the great wind, and found after in the Bay of Gregory of the Golden Mouth, and carried up the two of them on the one plank, and in by that door. (*She pauses for a moment, the girls start as if they heard something through the door that is half-open behind them.*)

NORA (*in a whisper*). Did you hear that, Cathleen? Did you hear a noise in the northeast?

CATHLEEN (*in a whisper*). There's someone after crying out by the seashore.

MAURYA (*continues without hearing anything*). There was Sheamus and his father, and his own father again, were lost in a dark night, and not a stick or sign was seen of them when the sun went up. There was Patch after was drowned out of a curagh that turned over. I was sitting here with Bartley, and he a baby, lying on my two knees, and I seen two women, and three women, and four women coming in, and they crossing themselves, and not saying a word. I looked out then, and there were men coming after them, and they holding a thing in the half of a red sail, and water dripping out of it—it was a dry day, Nora—and leaving a track to the door. (*She pauses again with her hand stretched out toward the door. It opens softly and old women begin to come in, crossing themselves on the threshold, and kneeling down in front of the stage with red petticoats over their heads.*)

MAURYA (*half in a dream, to* CATHLEEN). Is it Patch, or Michael, or what is it at all?

CATHLEEN. Michael is after being found in the far north, and when he is found there how could he be here in this place?

MAURYA. There does be a power of young men floating round in the sea, and what way would they know if it was Michael they had, or another man like him, for when a man is nine days in the sea, and the wind blowing, it's hard set his own mother would be to say what man was it.

CATHLEEN. It's Michael, God spare him, for they're after sending us a bit of his clothes from the far north. (*She reaches out and hands* MAURYA *the clothes that belonged to Michael.* MAURYA *stands up slowly, and takes them in her hands.* NORA *looks out.*)

NORA. They're carrying a thing among them and there's water dripping out of it and leaving a track by the big stones.

CATHLEEN (*in a whisper to the women who have come in*). Is it Bartley it is?

ONE OF THE WOMEN. It is surely, God rest his soul.

(*Two younger* WOMEN *come in and pull out the table. Then* MEN *carry in the body of* BARTLEY, *laid on a plank, with a bit of a sail over it, and lay it on the table.*)

CATHLEEN (*to the women, as they are doing so*). What way was he drowned?

ONE OF THE WOMEN. The gray pony knocked him into the sea, and he was washed out where there is a great surf on the white rocks.

(MAURYA *has gone over and knelt down at the head of the table. The women are keening softly and swaying themselves with a slow movement.* CATHLEEN *and* NORA *kneel at the other end of the table. The men kneel near the door.*)

MAURYA (*raising her head and speaking as if she did not see the people around her*). They're all gone now, and there isn't anything more the sea can do to me. . . . I'll have no call now to be up crying and praying when the wind breaks from the south, and you can hear the surf is in the east, and the surf is in the west, making a great stir with the two noises, and they hitting one on the other. I'll have no call now to be going down and getting Holy Water in the dark nights after Samhain,[1] and I won't care what way the sea is when the other women will be keening. (*To* NORA) Give me the Holy Water, Nora, there's a small sup still on the dresser.

(NORA *gives it to her.*)

MAURYA (*drops Michael's clothes across* BARTLEY's *feet, and sprinkles the Holy Water over him*). It isn't that I haven't prayed for you, Bartley, to the Almighty God. It isn't that I haven't said prayers in the dark night till you wouldn't know what I'd be saying; but it's a great rest I'll have now, and it's time surely. It's a great rest I'll have now, and great sleeping in the long nights after Samhain, if it's only a bit of wet flour we do have to eat, and maybe a fish that would be

---

[1] **Samhain:** Feast of All Saints.

stinking. (*She kneels down again, crossing herself, and saying prayers under her breath.*)

CATHLEEN (*to an old* MAN). Maybe yourself and Eamon would make a coffin when the sun rises. We have fine white boards herself bought, God help her, thinking Michael would be found, and I have a new cake you can eat while you'll be working.

THE OLD MAN (*looking at the boards*). Are there nails with them?

CATHLEEN. There are not, Colum; we didn't think of the nails.

ANOTHER MAN. It's a great wonder she wouldn't think of the nails, and all the coffins she's seen made already.

CATHLEEN. It's getting old she is, and broken.

(MAURYA *stands up again very slowly and spreads out the pieces of Michael's clothes beside the body, sprinkling them with the last of the Holy Water.*)

NORA (*in a whisper to* CATHLEEN). She's quiet now and easy, but the day Michael was drowned you could hear her crying out from this to the spring well. It's fonder she was of Michael, and would anyone have thought that?

CATHLEEN (*slowly and clearly*). An old woman will be soon tired with anything she will do, and isn't it nine days herself is after crying and keening, and making great sorrow in the house?

MAURYA (*puts the empty cup mouth downward on the table, and lays her hands together on* BARTLEY'S *feet*). They're all together this time, and the end is come. May the Almighty God have mercy on Bartley's soul, and on Michael's soul, and on the souls of Sheamus and Patch, and Stephen and Shawn (*bending her head*); and may he have mercy on my soul, Nora, and on the soul of every one is left living in the world. (*She pauses, and the keen rises a little more loudly from the women, then sinks away.*)

MAURYA (*continuing*). Michael has a clean burial in the far north, by the grace of the Almighty God. Bartley will have a fine coffin out of the white boards, and a deep grave surely. What more can we want than that? No man at all can be living forever, and we must be satisfied. (*She kneels down again and the curtain falls slowly.*)

What forewarnings of doom can you find in this play?

Some tragedies suggest that a hero's life is controlled by fate, that he is caught in a destiny he can do nothing about. Is Maurya expressing a fatalistic outlook when she says "there isn't anything more the sea can do to me"? Why? How is fate involved in the old woman's quest for Leza? Can the idea of fate lead to a feeling of nothingness? How?

The World

Take no oath, take no oath
    by the sod you stand upon:
you walk it short while
    but your burial is long.

Pay no heed, pay no heed
    to the world and its way;
give no love, give no love
    to what lasts but a day.

Have no care, have no care
    for the meaningless earth;
lay not hold, lay not hold
    on its gaiety and mirth.

A man fair of face
    was here yesterday;
now he is nothing
    but blood beneath clay.

The world is running out
    like the ebbing sea:
fly far from it
    and seek safety.

Translated from the Irish by James Carney

Do you think that the human experiences described in these last six selections are presented as "meaningless"? Does the Irish poet, in "The World," suggest that "safety" can be found somewhere?

HORROR

The Fire

This is a portion of a chapter from the book *Hiroshima*, about the nuclear bombardment of that Japanese city.

All day, people poured into Asano Park. This private estate was far enough away from the explosion so that its bamboos, pines, laurel, and maples were still alive, and the green place invited refugees—partly because they believed that if the Americans came back, they would bomb only buildings; partly because the foliage seemed a center of coolness and life, and the estate's exquisitely precise rock gardens, with their quiet pools and arching bridges, were very Japanese, normal, secure; and also partly (according to some who were there) because of an irresistible, atavistic urge to hide under leaves. Mrs. Nakamura and her children were among the first to arrive, and they settled in the bamboo grove near the river. They all felt terribly thirsty, and they drank from the river. At once they were nauseated and began vomiting, and they retched the whole day. Others were also nauseated; they all thought (probably because of the strong odor of ionization, an "electric smell" given off by the bomb's fission) that they were sick from a gas the Americans had dropped. When Father Kleinsorge and the other priests came into the park, nodding to their friends as they passed, the Nakamuras were all sick and prostrate. A woman named Iwasaki, who lived in the neighborhood of the mission and who was sitting near the Nakamuras, got up and asked the priests if she should stay where she was or go with them. Father Kleinsorge said, "I hardly know where the safest place is." She stayed there, and later in the day, though she had no visible wounds or burns, she died. The priests went farther along the river and settled down in some underbrush. Father LaSalle lay down and went right to sleep. The theological student, who was wearing slippers, had carried with him a bundle of clothes, in which he had packed two pairs of leather shoes. When he sat down with the others, he found that the bundle had broken open and a couple of shoes had fallen out and now he had only two lefts. He retraced his steps and found one right. When he rejoined the priests, he said, "It's funny, but things don't matter any more. Yesterday, my shoes were my most important possessions. Today, I don't care. One pair is enough."

Father Cieslik said, "I know. I started to bring my books along, and then I thought, 'This is no time for books.' "

When Mr. Tanimoto, with his basin still in his hand, reached the park, it was very crowded, and to distinguish the living from the dead was not easy, for most of the people lay still, with their eyes open. To Father Kleinsorge, an Occidental, the silence in the grove by the river, where hundreds of gruesomely wounded suffered together, was one of the most dreadful and awesome phenomena of his whole experience. The hurt ones were quiet; no one wept, much less screamed in pain; no one complained; none of the many who died did so noisily; not even the children cried; very few people even spoke. And when Father Kleinsorge gave water to some whose faces had been almost blotted out by flash burns, they took their share and then raised themselves a little and bowed to him, in thanks.

Mr. Tanimoto greeted the priests and then looked around for other friends. He saw Mrs. Matsumoto, wife of the director of the Methodist School, and asked her if she was thirsty. She was, so he went to one of the pools in the Asano's rock gardens and got water for her in his basin. Then he decided to try to get back to his church. He went into Noboricho by the way the priests had taken as they escaped, but he did not get far; the fire along the streets was so fierce that he had to turn back. He walked to the river bank and began to look for a boat in which he might carry some of the most severely injured across the river from Asano Park and away from the spreading fire. Soon he found a good-sized pleasure punt drawn up on the bank, but in and around it was an awful tableau—five dead men, nearly naked, badly burned, who must have expired more or less all at once, for they were in attitudes which suggested that they had been working together to push the boat down into the river. Mr. Tanimoto lifted them away from the boat, and as he did so, he experienced such horror at disturbing the dead—preventing them, he momentarily felt, from launching their craft and going on their ghostly way—that he said out loud, "Please forgive me for taking this boat. I must use it for others, who are alive." The punt was heavy, but he managed to slide it into the water. There were no oars, and all he could find for propulsion was a thick bamboo pole. He worked the boat upstream to the most crowded part of the park and began to ferry the wounded. He could pack ten or twelve into the boat for each crossing, but as the river was too deep in the center to pole his way across, he had to paddle with the bamboo, and consequently each trip took a very long time. He worked several hours that way.

Early in the afternoon, the fire swept into the woods of Asano Park. The first Mr. Tanimoto knew of it was when, returning in his boat, he saw that a great number of people had moved toward the riverside. On touching the bank, he went up to investigate, and when he saw the fire, he shouted, "All the young men who are not badly hurt come with me!" Father Kleinsorge moved Father Schiffer and Father LaSalle close to the edge of the river and asked people there to get them across if the fire came too near, and then joined Tanimoto's volunteers. Mr. Tanimoto sent some to look for buckets and basins and told others to beat the burning underbrush with their clothes; when utensils were at hand, he formed a bucket chain from one of the pools in the rock gardens. The team fought the fire for more than two hours, and gradually defeated the flames. As Mr. Tanimoto's men worked, the frightened people in the park pressed closer and closer to the river, and finally the mob began to force some of the unfortunates who were on the very bank into the water. Among those driven into the river and drowned were Mrs. Matsumoto, of the Methodist School, and her daughter.

When Father Kleinsorge got back after fighting the fire, he found Father Schiffer still bleeding and terribly pale. Some Japanese stood around and stared at him, and Father Schiffer whispered, with a weak smile, "It is as if I were already dead." "Not yet," Father Kleinsorge said. He had brought Dr. Fujii's first-aid kit with him, and he had noticed Dr. Kanda in the crowd, so he sought him out and asked him if he would dress Father Schiffer's bad cuts. Dr. Kanda had seen his wife and daughter dead in the ruins of his hospital; he sat now with his head in his hands. "I can't do anything," he said. Father Kleinsorge bound more bandage around Father Schiffer's head, moved him to a steep place, and settled him so that his head was high, and soon the bleeding diminished.

The roar of approaching planes was heard about this time. Someone in the crowd near the Nakamura family shouted, "It's some Grummans coming to strafe us!" A baker named Nakashima stood up and commanded, "Everyone who is wearing anything white, take it off." Mrs. Nakamura took the blouses off her children, and opened her umbrella and made them get under it. A great number of people, even badly burned ones, crawled into bushes and stayed there until the hum, evidently of a reconnaissance or weather run, died away.

It began to rain. Mrs. Nakamura kept her children under the umbrella. The drops grew abnormally large, and someone shouted, "The Americans are dropping gasoline. They're going to set fire to us!" (This alarm stemmed from one of the theories being passed through the park as to why so much of Hiroshima had burned: it was that a single plane had sprayed gasoline on the city and then somehow set fire to it in one flashing moment.) But the drops were palpably water, and as they fell, the wind grew stronger and stronger, and suddenly—probably because of the tremendous convection set up by the blazing city—a whirlwind ripped through the park. Huge trees crashed down; small ones were uprooted and flew into the air. Higher, a wild array of flat things revolved in the twisting funnel—pieces of iron roofing, papers, doors, strips of matting. Father Kleinsorge put a piece of cloth over Father Schiffer's eyes, so that the feeble man would not think he was going crazy. The gale blew Mrs. Murata, the mission housekeeper, who was sitting close by the river, down the embankment at a shallow, rocky place, and she came out with her bare feet bloody. The vortex moved out onto the river, where it sucked up a waterspout and eventually spent itself.

After the storm, Mr. Tanimoto began ferrying people again, and Father Kleinsorge asked the theological student to go across and make

his way out to the Jesuit Novitiate at Nagatsuka, about three miles from the center of town, and to request the priests there to come with help for Fathers Schiffer and LaSalle. The student got into Mr. Tanimoto's boat and went off with him. Father Kleinsorge asked Mrs. Nakamura if she would like to go out to Nagatsuka with the priests when they came. She said she had some luggage and her children were sick—they were still vomiting from time to time, and so, for that matter, was she—and therefore she feared she could not. He said he thought the fathers from the Novitiate could come back the next day with a pushcart to get her.

Late in the afternoon, when he went ashore for a while, Mr. Tanimoto, upon whose energy and initiative many had come to depend, heard people begging for food. He consulted Father Kleinsorge, and they decided to go back into town to get some rice from Mr. Tanimoto's Neighborhood Association shelter and from the mission shelter. Father Cieslik and two or three others went with them. At first, when they got among the rows of prostrate houses, they did not know where they were; the change was too sudden, from a busy city of two hundred and forty-five thousand that morning to a mere pattern of residue in the afternoon. The asphalt of the streets was still so soft and hot from the fires that walking was uncomfortable. They encountered only one person, a woman, who said to them as they passed, "My husband is in those ashes." At the mission, where Mr. Tanimoto left the party, Father Kleinsorge was dismayed to see the building razed. In the garden, on the way to the shelter, he noticed a pumpkin roasted on the vine. He and Father Cieslik tasted it and it was good. They were surprised at their hunger, and they ate quite a bit. They got out several bags of rice and gathered up several other cooked pumpkins and dug up some potatoes that were nicely baked under the ground, and started back. Mr. Tanimoto rejoined them on the way. One of the people with him had some cooking utensils. In the park, Mr. Tanimoto organized the lightly wounded women of his neighborhood to cook. Father Kleinsorge offered the Nakamura family some pumpkin, and they tried it, but they could not keep it on their stomachs. Altogether, the rice was enough to feed nearly a hundred people.

Just before dark, Mr. Tanimoto came across a twenty-year-old girl, Mrs. Kamai, the Tanimotos' next-door neighbor. She was crouching on the ground with the body of her infant daughter in her arms.

The baby had evidently been dead all day. Mrs. Kamai jumped up when she saw Mr. Tanimoto and said, "Would you please try to locate my husband?"

Mr. Tanimoto knew that her husband had been inducted into the Army just the day before; he and Mrs. Tanimoto had entertained Mrs. Kamai in the afternoon, to make her forget. Kamai had reported to the Chugoku Regional Army Headquarters—near the ancient castle in the middle of town—where some four thousand troops were stationed. Judging by the many maimed soldiers Mr. Tanimoto had seen during the day, he surmised that the barracks had been badly damaged by whatever it was that had hit Hiroshima. He knew he hadn't a chance of finding Mrs. Kamai's husband, even if he searched, but he wanted to humor her. "I'll try," he said.

"You've got to find him," she said. "He loved our baby so much. I want him to see her once more."

John Hersey

What seem to be the most horrible details in this selection? Why? Does it affect your reactions to this passage to realize that it is a documentary account of actual events, whereas most (though not all) of what you've read in this book is imaginative literature?

How can the "death" that man creates be seen as victimizing the citizens of Hiroshima? How are these people different from the people in the phase "Pride and Death" in this Second Story?

Experience can be seen in two ways. There can be experience of the conflict between good and evil by those who are themselves evil or who are at least partially to blame for what happens to them. (List such characters from this Second Story.) Or there can be experience of evil simply through suffering it, through being burdened with the sorrows of a bitter existence. (Make a list of the characters who know this kind of experience in the Second Story.)

The Coming of the Plague

September was when it began.
Locusts dying in the fields; our dogs
Silent, moving like shadows on a wall;
And strange worms crawling; flies of a kind
We had never seen before; huge vineyard moths;
Badgers and snakes, abandoning
Their holes in the field; the fruit gone rotten;
Queer fungi sprouting; the woods
Covered with spiderwebs; black vapors
Rising from the earth—all these,
And more, began that fall. Ravens flew round
The hospital in pairs. Where there was water,
We could hear the sound of beating clothes
All through the night. We could not count
All the miscarriages, the quarrels, the jealousies.
And one day in a field I saw
A swarm of frogs, swollen and hideous,
Hundreds upon hundreds, sitting on each other,
Huddled together, silent, ominous,
And heard the sound of rushing wind.

Weldon Kees

Contrast this poem with "The Animals" in the First Story. Reread the
two selections that open the First Story. By the end of this Second Story,
do you think that darkness has "mastered" the light? Do you think
there will have to be more "Stories"?

TRAGEDY

This Second Story can also be seen in the three ways in which we suggested you look at the First Story. The individual selections are followed by questions, some of which invite you to examine details, that is, to take a "close-up" view. You also have probably discussed what the selections tell you about events, things, and people in the real world. When we stand back now and take a long-range view of the Second Story as a whole, we see that it, too, has an overall "structure." Like the First Story, this second one is also made up of independent items and of fragments of larger works (for example, Dick Gregory's story, "Not Poor, Just Broke," is part of a book he wrote about his life). But all these independent selections and the fragments have been arranged in an order. This order takes the "shape" of another kind of story, which we call tragedy.

We have already said that all stories have "shapes." They move in either of two directions. If the story has a happy (or comic) shape, we say it moves upward; if the story has a sad (or tragic) shape, we say it moves downward. All the selections in the Second Story, with the exception of *Abraham and Isaac,* show a downward movement. Moreover, the selections as arranged here move downward from phase to phase. The Second Story ends with the phase called "Horror," which describes situations that are at the lowest point of man's existence.

We have set forth six phases in the Second Story. The first three are somewhat similar to the first three in romance. In these phases, in both Stories, we read about beautiful persons and things. But in tragedy these beautiful persons or things are destroyed or very badly hurt: the leaping buck; Connla; Lucy Gray; Adam and Eve; Langston Hughes' sweet and wonderful words, *Freedom* and *Liberty;* the young Dick Gregory; David; the girl who loved the butcher boy; the black children in James Baldwin's essay; the Indian man searching for his dead wife. These beautiful persons and things are idealized,

or very good, or innocent. And somehow they are all too capable of being hurt. We say they are "innocent" either because they have done nothing to deserve the evil that has come to them, or because they begin as "innocents" and something happens which forces them to experience or "know" first-hand the clash between good and evil.

In the first phase, called "Destruction of the Beautiful," the stag, Connla, and Lucy Gray are as close as possible to real innocence. These victims have no understanding of evil. Death comes to them through no fault of their own. Their stories are tragic because what we feel *should* happen does *not* happen.

In the second phase, called "The Death of Innocence," the emphasis is on the brutal ways in which innocence itself, or inexperience, encounters the bleak realities of life, and is changed by them. Notice the sense of shame that the once-innocent Dick Gregory is made to feel. Notice Bob's dilemma in the long narrative poem, "David": suddenly, in one day, he must face what he did to his friend, and in so doing he loses his youth and his innocence. The apple that is "heavy as the world" in Shigeji's poem *is* the knowledge of the clash of good and evil, and it is heavy knowledge.

The third phase, called "Triumph and Defeat," is somewhat like the "Quest" phase of romance. Here we find an emphasis on quests and on heroic achievement, but these quests either fail or they succeed in the midst of tragedy or threatened destruction. The Indian man succeeds in bringing his wife back from the land of the dead, but because he fails at the last minute he loses her a second time and dies himself. James Baldwin describes the courage of the black children who continue their heroic quest despite hostility. The singer of "The Battle Hymn of the Republic" calls on people to quest for freedom, and to die for it if necessary. Many people believe that the greatest heroism possible is to give one's life freely for others. This is the triumph in Beowulf's death. Isaac, with his pathetic obedience and willingness to be a "sacrifice," illustrates this kind of savior-hero particularly clearly, though in this play divine intervention prevents catastrophe from taking place. The savior-hero who is not saved at the last minute, as Isaac was, is referred to in the last stanza of "The Battle Hymn of the Republic."

When we pass on to the fourth phase of tragedy, called "Pride and Death," we are moving out of the world where disaster strikes innocence and entering instead a world where disaster comes to people who are more experienced and more fully aware of evil. The dignity and courage which we have found in other heroes still cling to the characters here. Two of these tragic figures, Lucifer and Belshazzar, are clearly flawed and guilty, but they are still somehow heroic, indicating that it is not only pure and good characters who can dominate tragedies. John Henry is an admirable figure. He is strong, but he is stubborn, and he drives so hard to compete against a machine that he breaks his heart and dies. He is different from ordinary people just as a giant redwood—in its size, its capacity for being struck by lightning, and its loneliness—is different from an ordinary tree. Many of the individual tragic heroes in the first four phases of this Second Story exhibit this quality of "being different" from ordinary human beings; Connla, Abraham, Beowulf, Lucifer, and Belshazzar are other examples of such greatness.

With the fifth phase, called "Nothingness," we have people who "know" evil simply because they suffer. They are burdened with bitter experience. The old woman who looks for Leza is a symbol of man's ancient search for the meaning of undeserved suffering and evil in the world. The old woman Maurya, in *Riders to the Sea*, recognizes that she is completely helpless before the fate that destroys her menfolk one by one. In Claude Brown's essay "Where does one run to . . . ?" the black people who go north to a large city move from one kind of poverty into another, and from one kind of bondage into another— "from the fire into the frying pan," as the author puts it. The blues singer of "In the Evenin', Mama," has lost his little woman, and his  song expresses tragic "nothingness" because he knows that he can do nothing about his lonesomeness except sing about it. All the characters in this phase of tragedy seem to be less free than the readers. That is why we can say that the Second Story moves farther downward than the First Story, to a point of human existence that is below anything imagined in romance. The science fiction tale "If I Forget Thee, Oh Earth . . . ," in the First Story, ends at a point "above" any of the tragedies in this Second Story. The moon-exiles in that story are alive, and at least they hope to go back someday to their home on earth. The tragic figures in the Second Story have nowhere to go. No magic will work for them. If these figures were in the imagined world of romance, where wishes *do* come true, they could, like Jack in "Soldier Jack," put Death in a bag. But in tragedy there is no enchantment to save the victim.

The final phase of the Second Story is called "Horror." It takes place in a world of shock and horror. It deals with situations of unrelieved cruelty and outrage. The victims in this phase are in such great agony that they have moved to a point of existence that is even "lower" than that of the victims in the phase "Nothingness." Death seems to be the only way to escape from their dreadful situation. The Japanese of Hiroshima who suffer silently and politely have been totally victimized by a force beyond their understanding or control. They are the least "free" in a catalogue of tragic figures whose freedom has relentlessly narrowed down throughout the Second Story.

The basic form of tragedy is a story of revenge. The hero somehow provokes hatred or ill will, or simply receives it through no fault of his own. The working out of the vengeance brings about the catastrophe that defeats him. The avengers vary, from the impersonal forces of nature in "Lucy Gray" and *Riders to the Sea* to the divine wrath that is turned against Lucifer and Belshazzar. Sometimes the characters in tragedy know what is happening to them and yet are powerless to stop it. This increases the tragic effect. By the time tragic action is complete, we have seen the loss of a human life that might have been free and good.

In one sense, every man becomes a tragic figure merely by being born, because every new birth eventually leads to the coming of another death. James Baldwin expresses this tragic view of life when he says, "Life is tragic simply because the earth turns." Many writers communicate a sense that man himself has lost an originally higher destiny. This means that all men can be seen as tragic figures who have, like Lucifer, fallen from a great height. Adam and Eve in Paradise thus are seen as the first tragic hero and heroine. On one side of them is opportunity for freedom and joy in the green world of Eden; on the other side is the absence of freedom and joy. In losing Paradise, Adam, or man (the Hebrew word *Adam* means "man"), and his companion become subject to death. And even as human life is subject to a fate involving death, so nature itself dies. One poem in this Story says that "Adam walks in the cold night/Wilderness, waste wood." This identification of the death of the natural world with the death of innocence or with human death recurs again and again in tragic literature. Margaret in Hopkins' poem really mourns for herself when she mourns over the dead leaves.

Looking at the total shape of this Second Story, then, we can see that it moves relentlessly downward. In the first three phases, tragedy strikes mostly heroic people who are given the greatest possible dignity. In the last three phases, destructive experiences come to increasingly realistic, and therefore flawed, people. The Story moves away from accounts of children and young people into accounts of older persons who are weighed down with experience and suffering. "The Coming of the Plague" describes the lowest point in all these human experiences. In this poem, man is in a plague-stricken world, full of petty quarrels and jealousies, looking at hundreds and hundreds of swollen, hideous frogs as they sit huddled on top of each other, silent.

Index of Authors and Titles

E
F
G
H
I
J